RUSSELL GRANT'S

Astrological Diet Book

L

Dedicated to my lovely Libran mother who is an eternal student of diet and has never lost a pound.

———

RUSSELL GRANT'S

Astrological Diet Book

Lennard Publishing
1988

Lennard Publishing
a division of Lennard Books Ltd

Lennard House
92 Hastings Street
Luton, Beds LU1 5BH

British Library Cataloguing-in-Publication Data

Grant, Russell
Russell Grant's astrological diet book.
1. Physical fitness. Slimming. Diet
Astrological aspects
I. Title
133.5′86132′5

ISBN 1-85291-007-0

First published 1988
© Russell Grant 1988

Phototypeset in Galliard and Electra
by Goodfellow & Egan Limited, Cambridge

Printed in Great Britain
by William Clowes, Beccles, Suffolk

Cover design by Pocknell and Co.
Editor Marion Davies

Contents

Why I changed my eating habits

I've always considered myself a Tate & Lyle tot 'cos I was born in 1952 just after the bombing stopped, when food and fancies were still in short supply. My Mum, bless her, used to say, "Eat it all up, don't leave anything on your plate, there are people who would give their eyeteeth for that food!" So I had all the agonising anguish of not being allowed to leave the minutest morsel and that's really how Russell became a roly-poly!

It wasn't so bad on tour in my early teens as I was only 10 stone. In those days I wasn't too fussed about food, but like most lads of my age I drank like a fish and smoked like a chimney. But in my mid-twenties I got wise to the health hazards and of course, what happened? Everytime I fancied a fag I'd grab a cheese sandwich or lashings of lovely butter and fresh crusty bread from the bakery, yummee!, and my weight soared to 18½ stone!

When I was in BBC TV's 'Breakfast Time', they bunged in a hot chocolate machine specially for me, 'cos I never touch tea or coffee – not my cup of tea! Coffee (instant that is, not the perky kind) is loaded with aluminium and too much coffee can shrink the old brain, so I haven't had a bean for years. I still like a cup of Rosie Lee but I've turned to herbal teas since my diet and I keep a collection of about twenty different herbal teas which double as a mild diuretic.

Before that, my real wayward weakness was hot chocolate and every morning, before the breakfast show, I'd be found sitting with sensational Selina Scott, sipping away, while we discussed the script of the day, and when I'd go into the studio, there'd be two more cups of chocks waiting for me! Word of my wicked weakness spread, and even the Beeb Wales in Llandaff, Cardiff materialised a machine for me and I'd be scoffing it before shows.

'Breakfast Time' was terribly tiring 'cos it messed up my metabolism. When it finished at 9.30 a.m., my mind insisted it was lunchtime and I could quite merrily munch my way through shepherds pie and veggies as I'd been fighting fit since 4.00 a.m. By 3.00 in the afternoon, I was dying for my dinner! Picture the problems it posed for me! Because I was rushing round and round, I'd scoff several sarnies just to keep going. I normally went to bed between 9.00 and 10.00 p.m.

I quite enjoy bedding down early, (to sleep of course!). As an Aquarian, I'm opposite to the owl, more like the lark, so emerging early for breakfast telly wasn't too troublesome and tedious for me. It was 'Breakfast Time' that really created my career and suddenly I was at it all the hours of the day and more. I cast astrological charts, and scribed for magazines as well as writing about the stars, and I put in personal appearances. All the time I was picking and pecking at palatable portions, and my weight was steadily soaring. I was right out of a routine. It barely bothered me 'till one day I was battling with the stairs up to my top floor office when I started panting and had pains across my chest. My heart was pounding and I was really knackered. I thought my end had come and was totally terrified. It flashed through my mind that my granddad died of a heart attack at fifty-two. When he died, the doctor said he had the ticker of a man of eighty and his death was due to his weight – over 20 stone! So, I thought to myself, Russell, you're not ready to kick the bucket! I dashed off to my doctor and she agreed that I wanted to lose weight but she couldn't help me. I left her office feeling dreadfully down and dejected and as I drove home, a car drew alongside and a bloke bellowed out, "Hello, Russell, you big fat bastard, how are you?" I know he was only saying this as a joke but it really hit home.

Anyway it did the trick, and made me determined to slim down. I decided to do it decently with Astrology. Full Moons signal the closing of a cycle and the next one was in Capricorn in June (of 1986 that is). So I started from there. The secret was to change my whole lifestyle and diet style – not an easy errand believe me! In the beginning I'd say to myself, "I'll bypass breakfast today, I'll be a good boy." and then by 11.00 I was desperate for nosh, and positively drooling, so what did I do? I'd nibble a little of this and a little of that and it soon became an obsession. My one wild weakness, 'specially if I'm feeling fretful, is guzzling and gorging. I go a bit wild and woolly and binge like mad. So I resolved to revolutionise my eating habits! This diet would be demonstrably different!

When I wake in the morning now I don't want grub, but at about 9.00 I tuck into something like All-Bran or Rice Krispies (a boost for the bowels!), a slice of toast and a poached egg. I always tried to make my main meal in the middle of the day, so I could work it off before bedtime! In the evening, I'd stick to a light meal, perhaps some poached fish or a tuna fish sarnie, and even now that I tuck away three meals a day again, I've contrived to control my weight.

I've seen folk get faddish about dieting like 'there must be at least seven calories in that grain of rice' and that can drive you daffy as well as lead to neurotic nasties like Anorexia Nervosa. So I'm still learning, even this late in life, not to go over the top about my diet. If I go on a rare holiday, I try not to be a stuffy old sourpuss, and starving myself like I did a bit at the beginning of my diet 'cos I was scared stiff that if I had fish and chips, I'd end up stuffing on them. But I found that I didn't crave the calories and that I had learned a whole new dietary lifestyle.

I'm lucky as an Aquarian, 'cos I have an immovable willpower. Jean Rook of the Daily Express once said, "This man may look cuddly and sweet but he has a will of iron," and it's true. If I really set my sights on something then I say "How can I make this work for me?" but it has to hail from the heart. All Sun signs have strong and weak points, for instance trustworthy Taureans and luscious Librans can't pass a chocolate shop! Aquarians, being one of the air signs, have a higher metabolic rate so they burn off excess adipose. Same story for the fiery folk of Aries, Leo and Sagittarius. Geminis, Librans and Aquarians are wildly wayward with their noshing, picking here, picking there, nibbling, gnawing and chewing. Taureans and Cancerians love mountains of marvellous food, 'cos the way to their tickers is very definitely through their tums! Each celestial sign has its own particular passions and weaknesses.

But whatever your sign, if you want to shed the stones it's a psychological process and you've got to be steadfast, strong and single-minded! No point starting a diet if you're haphazard and halfhearted about it!

The first day of my diet, I really heaved body and soul together and had an all liquid day. I drank litres of lemon juice (a great purger and cleanser) and promising myself a prize was very important, so every day I'd reward myself with a chocolate flake or a biscuit or some honey. Just a little luxury to make life worth living again! I thought of it there, my tasty tidbit, and that encouraged me to endure the day. Once I'd scoffed it, I could savour the thought of tomorrow's tasty treat! Fruit followed every plate of wholemeal, whole foods, brown rice and wholewheat spaghetti. I abandoned myself to dynamic dieting, did lots of stir fried in my wonderful wok, using a soupçon of sun flower oil, and fought off all animal fats.

My torso trembled from a series of light exercises, keep-fit such as touching my toes and lying on my back and pulling up – a shock to the system at the start! I still do these exercises in the morning and evening. I also believe that walking is an excellent exercise and I always plod up and down stairs and never take the easy way in lifts. I drink gallons of water, to flush the system through and have a clearout, and have two glasses of water before each meal. I drink lovely, refreshing British bubbly bottled water. (Not too much Perrier as it's salty.) If I was downright desperate during those early dieting days I'd knock back a food supplement drink.

After three brilliant years on 'Breakfast Time', I went over to work on wacky TV AM and the eats in the canteen there are irresistible! I do indulge in a good old British breakfast now, maybe an egg, juicy tomatoes and those marvellous, mouth-watering mushrooms. I endeavour to eat at regular times, 9.00 a.m., 1.00 p.m., and 5.00 p.m., never after 6.00 p.m. unless I'm out on the razzle or at a 'do' and then I change things round a bit. I appreciate that if you're hard at it 9 to 5 by the time you get back to hearth and home, it can be 7.00 p.m. before your evening meal. If that's the case, then for goodness sake, don't gobble and gorge 'cos your poor, pooped body hasn't got time to tackle tuck before you crash out. If I'm really ravenous at bedtime I sometimes have a sugar-free Ovaltine chocolate drink with only forty calories (who's counting!). You shouldn't starve yourself through the day thinking, "I'm a goody goody", 'cos (as I was told by Dr Alan Maryon Davies another Aquarian), if you don't feed it, your body can't click into action and your metabolism can't do its job. That makes sound sense really. It's probably why in the past when I've not been eating properly, yet when I've stood on the scales, I haven't wasted away to nothing, in fact I've put on a pound or two! The minute you eat, you set the body in merry motion and the metabolism motivated.

I hared off to a health farm once and it was the loneliest time of my life. I hated it! I gladly gave it up 'cos my Mum had a problem and it was a real relief to escape the horrors. I found it solitary, soul-destroying and stiff with lower middle class snobbery. I suppose you can't tar every health farm with the same brush but I really despised it and wild horses wouldn't drag me back again! Other folk might find being denied nosh works wonders but it was a bit of a con being charged £50 a day for water with a lemon slice stuck in it. I've tried all types of diets, the Cambridge Diet, the grapefruit diet, the Hollywood diet with exotic fruits like pineapple and mangoes, (the Carmen Miranda job), and the 'you name it' diet, but nothing pared those pounds off, so I decided to design my own exclusive diet through my Natal Chart.

I hope you see that I can only suggest and advise you or anyone and in the long run, you must devise a diet that definitely suits your individual makeup, taking account of your environment, lifestyle and routines. I knew my own zany, zestful lifestyle, so I took a long, lean look at that. I think the 1,000 Calorie Weight Watcher Diet is OK but I can't be fagged fiddling around with silly scales and saying this egg is two calories and this orange is seventy. I'm too impatient but it could suit statistically minded Sun signs like down to earth Virgos or Capricorns.

I don't booze at all now and only imbibe British sparkling spring water which I would recommend to everyone, 'specially lively Librans who love bubbly drinks. Jack Jones, the old Trade Union leader put me off some tap water for life, I won't let on why, 'cos it would make you reach for a bucket, but the only time I drink that processed rubbish is if I boil it first. I celebrated when I saw in the stars how Bucks Fizz would win the Eurovision Song Contest and drank to them with bubbly Bucks Fizz! This delightfully decadent drink of Champagne and orange juice is simply brimming with benefits for your diet as it's a great natural cleanser.

My old friend, Selina Scott is very deliberate with her diet and is sensible about her scoff – that's why she looks in such fantastically fine fettle! She'd be the first to confess that she was a chubby wee lassie when she worked up at Grampian TV. It was only puppy fat just like the perfectly polished and poised Princess of Wales before she lost lots of weight. Another mate of mine who looks absolutely marvellous is that sophisticated Scorpio Fenella Fielding. She once said to me, "Darling, if you don't have some fat in your diet, your skin will dry out. You must have some to keep it gleaming and glistening."

I delved into that advice and discovered it was true, so I started using a little St Ivel Gold unsalted butter which is half the calories of margarine or butter. Trouble is another of my wayward weaknesses is fat on meats, pork crackling or the crispy skin on lamb. Yummy! Most folk cut it off but I think it makes the meat more flavoursome. I started to pop that in as one of my little daily delights instead of chocolaty choices. I haven't had sugar for ages and if I feel an urge to sweeten anything, I use Canderel.

You could argue that if I had sugar, or even caffeine, I wouldn't crave for chocolate, but I'm not convinced. It's like innoculation, or drug addiction, they give you a little of the offending article to get you off it completely or the virus to make your body immune, so perhaps that applies to treats. Get away from valueless vanity and go for vital vivacity. The question is how do you feel? Is your health bad and negative 'cos of your nosh, and do you frighten yourself and think that your eating habits and lifestyle are killing you? My brother – yes we Grants are from solid stock! – lost a lot of weight on a herbal drinks diet.

Nowadays, I kick off, TV AM or not, at 6.00 a.m. with a warming, welcoming cup of herbal tea and then I work awhile on the word processor. If I feel a bit fazed and frazzled and I grab some grub just before 9.00 a.m. I watch the tropical fish flashing and flowing in their fish tank (so relaxing) and listen to Radio 4 and then I sometimes arrange my business meetings but most moments are spent doing the astrological calculations and writing the perennially popular Star columns for Woman's Own and a plethora of provincial papers, and holding more meetings between 11 and 1.00 p.m. Then lunch and I mustn't let that pass!

In the afternoon I answer my fan letters – over 1,000 a week which keeps Postman Pat on his points – and of course there are lots of phone calls when I'm home in Middlesex. When I'm visiting various TV studios or in the West End at meetings or business binges, I try to surreptitiously steer people to eateries which won't offer wicked temptations, like a Chinese, but I'm also a sucker for the Savoy Riverside Rooms. I may have mouth-watering melon and then a slice of rare roast beef or a succulent steak and salad and finish with fresh strawberries or fresh fruit.

After such a lunch meeting, I work in my office 'till 10.00 p.m. This is the scene six days a week. On Sundays, I get up at 8.00 a.m. and I work until 1.00 p.m., (not missing the wonderful Mrs Walker in The Archers!) then I'll maybe watch an afternoon flick. In the evening, I'm on the go from about 7.00 p.m. to 11.00 p.m. My two super-efficient secretaries help me with my heap of letters, but not my everyday work.

I sometimes bag a break 'cos it's a hard slog and I find that a doze in the afternoon between 2 and 3.00 p.m. fills me full of vim and vigour. It's said that a nap of an hour or in the afternoon is better than being abed all night. I never go on holiday abroad – I leave that to globetrotting gadabouts. I take my typewriter with me when I holiday at my breezy Blackpool, and I work from 9.00 a.m. to 1.00 p.m., free the afternoon and then work from 8.00 to 10.00 p.m. in the evening. It's always frantic, frenzied and frenetic, so I never really have a rest! Thinking about where you'd be without your local newspaper stars column drives me on!

I sometimes share supper out with close mates. I absolutely adore Chinese nosh and, when I met Christopher Biggins at a do thrown by Lisa Goddard and Alvin Stardust he introduced me to the theatrical Joe Allen's restaurant and their super fresh spinach salads, so I often go there with my editor at Woman's Own, Bridget Rowe to discuss future projects for the magazine. Mostly I'm at home, nose to grindstone, and 'cos I write all day, my mind is mulled by evening so I rest and relax or my brain will seize up and cease functioning.

As President of a Brookside Appreciation Society, I was chatting to Doreen Sloane, (who plays Annabel), who's lost a lot of weight. Two years ago in the TV Times 'My year ahead book' I said that she'd have to diet. She said, "It's so funny, Russell, I'd forgotten you'd written that, in fact I've lost 1½ stone." She did the controversial Cambridge Diet which some dieticians say is overly chemically orientated. I think it's OK in small doses.

My other relaxations are reading, i.e. the history of my own home county Middlesex and collecting maps and atlases of the British Isles. I've succeeded that great man Sir John Betjeman as patron of British County Heritage *and* founded the Friends of the County of Middlesex, and that's how I relax . . . really!

People ask me how I foresee my future. Well, I'd like to embark on astrological adventures in Australia and America but I'm very happy with my astrology work and lifestyle.

I'd like to write an erudite educational tome on Astrology and be recognised for it, but I think as age creeps up on me I shall become more seriously seeped in my conservation work and make sure we keep a grip on our country's history and heritage.

Before you begin

Astrology is for everyone, but our bodies aren't that different – after all, they're all related! So the following rules apply whatever your sign.

Before embarking on any diet, you should consult your doctor to make sure there are no physical reasons to prevent you going on your diet.

Basic rules to follow

1. You must drink two glasses of water before each meal.
2. **Your treat.** Choose your favourite fad like one chocolate or a slice of wholemeal bread and save it for the close of day or for a crisis point.
3. Try not to nosh in the night. Ideal eating time is 6.00 p.m. but I understand that's out if you're out at work.
4. This is an optional extra. If you're still in trouble and peckish then hop along to your nearest health food shop and ask them to recommend a fibre formula capsule that will help you control your eating and make your dieting a little easier.

You need to be psychologically prepared to really want to diet, be prepared to have smaller portions, less salt, and remember you cannot go back to your old eating habits.

ARIES

MARCH 21– APRIL 20

Aries the Ram. Let's take a look at your tireless traits and see if we can find a diet that will hold your interest long enough to be successful.

General Arian Characteristics

Aries is ruled by Martial Mars and is the first sign of the Zodiac. Maybe that's why, with ardent Arians, it's always numero uno, and first come, first served. This Fire Sign is fearfully impatient and when they want a deed done, it must be done yesterday. If it isn't they lose their rags and really let rip. Although highly inflammable and fierce, their tantrums and tirades are quickly forgotten. I have an Arian pal, and they make fine friends, who rings me at noon and can't fathom why I'm not free for lunch at 12.30! Bright and bubbly Arians, whose symbol is the rough and tumble Ram, have enthusiasm and energy and they're usually full of get-up-and-go. Like Sagittarians they are fearlessly frank, and the innocent object of their bluntness can end up being heartlessly hurt and upset. You see, these rambunctious rams put both hooves in it 'cos they're so naive. At work Arians need to be boss but with some of them it can be all brawn and little brain. They are brilliant at thinking up bright new ideas, but are often too impatient to see them through and they get bogged down with boredom. Rams hate desk jobs, they're far too dynamic and dramatic to sit still for long. Aries is first of the three fire signs, making them highly competitive and prepared to fight unflinchingly for what they want in life, often with their fists!

Arian love life

Randy Arians have a strong sex drive. Casanova was one, need I say more? Arian men have astonishingly active animal appeal and they generally have great bodies and look fit 'cos of their love of the athletic and sporty outdoor life. The Arian man is your eternal and everlasting bachelor and even when spliced, he'll still relish those stag nights and love to be one of the lads! They like to be seen with beautiful 'birds' and are foolishly flattered if their latest lady turns a few heads. I say their latest 'lady' 'cos once they've notched up another conquest, they're off to pastures new! So girls, if you fancy this philanderer, keep it to yourself, and let him dangle on a piece of string! Arians can be selfish lovers, plunged into the passion of the moment, but with these right old ravers there will be many moments! His passion often overwhelms him but when Miss Right comes round he will worship her at the risk of wrecking his life. Arian males make good dads, but beware that hot head and hasty temper. Arian women are attractive, independent and ambitious. It's a fatal flaw for this female to get hitched too early, and during her life she will amass many amorous admirers. They are phenomenally passionate pundits of sex. Arian maids adore making a spectacular entrance at a party or restaurant and tend to don bright and brilliant colours such as flaming scarlet to make sure they're noticed. They adore shopping for clobber, love to eat at expensive eateries and generally delight in dashing off their harassed husbands' hard earned cash.

Arian home life

Arians are away a lot so their homes are modern menages with all the latest labour saving devices. Their choice chamber is certainly the bedroom! They like a semblance of space, so their pads will be prodigious with panoramic views and preferably metropolitan. These are great showoffs so when they entertain, they invite everyone to eat at once, and their tables will be groaning with goodies. Active Arians are impatient shoppers and fume if forced to queue especially in a restaurant! They'd rather leave an excellent, expensive eaterie and career off to a naff caff 'cos they can have their desperate demands immediately met!

Arian health and eating habits

The trouble with ambitious Arians is that they'll start a diet but never finish it 'cos they get bored easily. They're too energetic to ease off, even when noshing, and can drive you crazy pacing up and down twixt courses. Spicy food is for them, and they're partial to pasta. They have a juvenile weakness for junk food and can wolf down a hamburger in a trice. This sign rules the head and that's where problems can come. Eyes and ears are prone to disease, and they are martyrs to migraines, headaches and frequent colds. Insomnia is another common cross to carry, 'cos they're so hotheaded and hurried they are accident prone, so slow down, Arians!

Famous people born under Aries

Marlon Brando, Charlie Chaplin, Julie Christie, Joan Crawford, Bette Davis, David Frost, Andrew Lloyd-Webber, Toscanini, Peter Ustinov, Van Gogh, Tennessee Williams.

People born on the cusp

If you're born on the cusp of Pisces, that is the 18th to the 22nd March, it could help you to stick to your diet 'cos you'll have filched a few fishy features.

If you're born on the cusp of Taurus, that is the 19th to the 22nd April, you may have some trusty Taurean traits to sap your Arian sizzles a little, especially when it comes to eating.

Your diet and essential foods

Let's put all this information together and try to find an easy diet for you with quick results so you won't have time to get bored.

Daily diet supplement

Your cell salt, Aries, is Potassium Phosphate which is needed for the growth and reproduction of nerve and brain cells. The migraines and headaches that Arians often suffer may be due to lack of Potassium Phosphate. Kali.Phos. pills are the homeopathically prepared biochemically active equivalent and I recommend that you take these along with your diet. They can be bought at any health food shop.

    1 Multivitamin with minerals
    1 Vitamin C (for those colds)
    1 B Complex
    Kali.Phos. pills

Here we go then, stick this list of foods up on your kitchen wall and make up your own range of recipes as you go along.

Positively no caffeinated coffee on your diet, you're far too energetic as it is. I've included dairy produce in this list, such as eggs, milk, cheese and butter but if you can, try to cut these out and see if that helps those horrid headaches.

Fruit	*Vegetables*	*Meat/Fish*	*Other Things*
Apples	Butter Beans	Lobster	Brown Rice
Pineapple	Broccoli	Trout	Spaghetti
Dates	Cabbage	Halibut	Macaroni
Lemons	Cauliflower	Salmon	Eggs
		(small tin)	
Fruit Juices	Celery	Chicken	Skimmed Milk
Melon	Cucumber	Turkey	Cheddar Cheese
Kiwis	Lettuce	Veal	Horseradish
Strawberries	Onions	Tuna	Jelly crystals
		(small tin)	(sugar free)
Oranges	Asparagus	Beef (cold)	Low Cal soups
Grapefruit	Tomatoes	Liver	Herbal teas
	Potato (1)		Raisins
	Spinach		Almonds
	Mushrooms		Walnuts
	Parsley		Bran
	Green Peppers		Yoghurt
	Avocado		Cinnamon
	Beetroot		Cottage Cheese

For cooking	A tiny drop of vegetable oil. Use a Wok if you have one, or cook with unsalted butter.
For salads	Make your own dressing without oil.

Right Arians I'll help you along with your first week of sensible, serious eating and then you're on your own!

DON'T FORGET, TWO GLASSES OF WATER BEFORE EVERY MEAL

DAY 1   Fruit only plus your two glasses of water before each course. This should help clear your system.

DAY 2   *Breakfast*
Bran with skimmed milk
Orange Juice
Lunch
Tuna (drain off oil or brine)
A small salad made of lettuce, tomato and cucumber
Your treat
Dinner
Asparagus
Chicken breast roast
Melon with cinnamon sprinkled over it.

DAY 3   *Breakfast*
1 boiled egg
Your treat
Grapefruit juice
Lunch
Green pepper (stuffed with tomatoes and mushrooms)
Dinner
Trout (grilled or poached) sprinkled with almonds
Braised celery
One new potato (if you must)
Jelly (try to find a sugar free jelly)

DAY 4   *Breakfast*
Bran again, this time covered with natural yoghurt
Mid-morning
Your treat
Lunch
A small salad made up of vegetables from your list.
Dinner
Beef (cold) with horseradish
Butter beans
Braised onions
Fresh fruit salad

DAY 5   *Breakfast*
Grapefruit
One egg scrambled

Lunch
Baked potato filled with cottage cheese
Dinner
Avocado with your dressing (no oil)
Spaghetti (wholewheat)
A sauce made of tomatoes, mushrooms and onions
Your treat *(for dessert)*

DAY 6   *Breakfast*
Fresh fruit
Lunch
Beetroot Soup (boil up some beets, 1 onion and a beef stock cube and blend, thin it out with water if necessary (very nourishing)
Your treat
Dinner
Liver (braised with tomatoes and onions)
Spinach
One new potato (if you must)
Slices of Pineapple

DAY 7   *Breakfast*
Bran with yoghurt
Orange juice
Lunch
Salmon (tinned, oil drained off)
A small salad
Dinner
Turkey
Braised celery
Strawberries
Your treat

Well, I quite enjoyed creating that crop of recipes for you. I'm sure you will dive into your diet with Arian dynamism. Don't forget your glasses of water before each meal. Bottled still water is best or bubbly bottled water, but if you can't afford such luxuries then use tap water and if you have time, boil it first. If you want a hot drink try herbal tea. Avoid coffee 'cos of your headaches and migraines.

TAURUS

APRIL 21 – MAY 21

Taureans love mountains of marvellous meals and it is a big decision for them to diet and give up a pet pastime, e.g. eating! Let's have a look at Taurean traits and see if we can find a diet that you'll find tolerable.

General Taurean characteristics

Taurus is a fixed sign and Taureans can be stubborn and mutinously mulish but this down-to-earth determination will eventually serve them well, and take them to the top of their livelihood ladder. This stolid stubbornness means Bulls are often blind to other folk's frame of mind.

Money and material matters are ruled by this sign and many Taureans become Midas-touched millionnaires. The perfect professions for them are with money matters like banks or The Stock Exchange. Everything they touch seems to turn to gold and most Bulls are worth a bob or two. Success in their careers means security for their loved ones and that's the largest-looming thing in their lives. Owning their own abode is their ultimate goal.

Taurus is the first of the Earth signs (it's no coincidence that they are so down-to-earth) and they cherish the charms of the countryside. Many Taureans fare well as farmers. Taureans are humans of habit, they relish routine and go weak at the knees at the thought of change. They want tomorrow to be a twin of today. Trusty Taureans make fabulous friends, but legendary lovers. They expect their chums to be staunch and steadfast and will give you everything in return.

Taureans have an air of solid self-confidence and they are divine dressers. They love the sensation of fine silks, leather and suedes. Touching is a sensuous essential to tactile Taureans and many of them become masseurs. They love art exhibitions, and probably have permanent pews at the opera house. Many Taureans dabble at drawing as a diversion whilst others air arias at the local amateur operatic society. Taurus controls the voice and many famous singers are born under this sign, e.g. Ella Fitzgerald, Barbra Streisand. These bovine

26

beauties are not late-nighters and they're too idle to dance at discos. No, the Bull's idea of bliss is a trip back to the native earth of their own country, a meander through meadows then the inevitable huge hamper jam-packed with gorgeous goodies and a bottle of red plonk! Bulls are brimful of fun with a wicked sense of humour. Many comedians are born under this sign, e.g. Terry Scott, Victoria Wood, Eric Sykes.

Taurean love life

Taurus, the Bull, has very expressive eyes and you can interpret their innermost thoughts without them uttering a word. Bulls don't become besotted very easily but these bovines become gentle and tender lovers and scorchingly sexy. They long for a loyal and loving married life and will prize their partners completely and try to possess them. Taureans rate loyalty and fidelity very highly and fight hard for their marriages. Bereaved or betrayed Bulls rarely bond again.

The Taurean man has a honed sense of humour and after a skinful the bovine beasts become positively bawdy and can go bananas. The way to a Taurean ticker is through his tum, so ladies, if you thrill to tender Taurus, wine and dine him with traditional tuck, soft lights, melodious music and gentle caresses and he will be putty in your hands. Once spliced they'll become possessive and positively green-eyed about you which, depending on your sign, can make you panic in your protective prison. Taurean men are passionate and sexy but as they relish routine sex can become as exciting as knicker elastic! Up to you to sprinkle spice into his soul.

The Taurean maiden is a home-bird and requires to put down roots. She is the Earth Mother of the Zodiac and her home, husband and hordes of kids become the whole of her happy life. (Her kitchen will be king too!) She'll make a marvellous mum and will adore her offspring. Torrid Taurean woman believes in fidelity and expects the same from her swain. She is ineffective at expressing her emotions and expects her partner to divine her deep love for him. If she forfeits him, she can't fathom out why. Taurean women are often attractive (e.g. Selina Scott) but are firmly unflirtatious as they find coyness to be sheer chicanery. They can be oh so sexily seductive when they want to be and call for lots of cuddles and kisses to turn them on. A Taurean female will never forgive or forget someone who wrongs her. She won't get even, like seething Scorpio, but will just dig her heels in and disregard her adversary for ever.

Taurean home life

The Taurean home would be spacious, and traditional and preferably in a pretty pastoral village setting. The decor will be down-to-earth colours, and the furnishings cosy and comfortable. They'll go for a gargantuan garden. If they are constrained in the city, you'll find a plethora of potted plants around the place. Taurus is ruled by voluptuous Venus, so their love of beauty is usually evident around their homes, like original paintings and antiques.

Their favourite room, (don't count the kitchen) is a sitting room crammed with creature comforts, and as they love animals you'll discover a (dreaming) dog basking in front of a blazing fire. If a Taurean asks you over to eat, don't nosh for a week before you go! Their very elegant table, choca with fine china, crystal and lace will be laden with goodies, a traditional roast is tops and you spend a leisurely evening, eating and drinking, (they love red wines) through countless courses. These happy hosts and hostesses love to see their guests enjoy their grub! There will be soft music in the background and you'll be soothed and salved. Lovely!

When shopping, Taureans demand truthfulness and thoroughness and look for freshness and quality in their foods, but their weakness is for fresh-baked bread and calorie-crammed cakes, and once they get a whiff they're lost! They adore a decent eatery that gives value for money and love to linger over a liqueur.

Taurean health and eating habits

A very robust sign! Apart from the Bull's food and sex binges this would be the healthiest sign in the heavens. They should ease off on the eating front 'cos they have worrying weight problems which temendously tax their tickers. Blithe bovines find it easy to relax by walking in the country or pottering among the plants. Taureans are prone to throat problems like thyroid glands, goitres or trouble with their vocal chords. They are also prone to asthma, bronchitis, diabetes and genital problems.

Famous people born under Taurus

Bing Crosby, Fred Astaire, Brahms, Hitler, Audrey Hepburn, Yehudi Menuhin, William Shakespeare, Orson Welles, Henry Fonda, Queen Elizabeth II.

People born on the cusp

If you're born on the cusp of Aries, that is the 19th to the 22nd April, though not as impulsive as Arians, you still have to tell yourself to slam on the brakes when it comes to eating.

If you're born on the cusp of Gemini, that is the 20th to the 24th May, you may have less of a problem 'cos you're always charging around and burning up those unwanted calories.

Your diet and essential foods

If only we can stop you munching so much, there should be no weight problem. Let's see what we can come up with for you, diet-wise.

Daily diet supplement

Your cell salt, Taurus, is Sodium Sulphate which helps break down foods and gets rid of excess water in the body. It is present in certain foods but it wouldn't hurt you to take Nat. Sulph. pills which are the homeopathically prepared biochemically active equivalent and they can be bought at health food shops.

1 Multivitamin with minerals
1 Vitamin C
Nat. Sulph. pills

OK here we go, here is a list of foods for you to stick up on your kitchen wall, select a menu for a week.

Fruit	Vegetables	Meat/Fish	Other Things
Apples	Cabbage	Chicken	Horseradish
Pineapple	Cucumber	Shrimp	Jelly crystals (sugar free)
Grapefruit	Lettuce	Liver	Eggs
Papaya	Tomatoes	Beef (cold)	Bran
Blackberries	Onions	Turkey	Almonds
Strawberries	Radishes	Sole	Skimmed milk
Oranges	Beetroots	Halibut	Cottage cheese
Lemons	Spinach	Frankfurter	Yoghurt

Grapes	Potato (1)	Tuna	Spaghetti (wholewheat)
Bananas	Mushrooms	Salmon	Brown Rice
Fruit juices	Green Pepper		
	Asparagus		
	Watercress		
	Sauerkraut		
	Broccoli		
	Avocado		
	Courgettes		

For cooking   A tiny drop of vegetable oil. Use a wok if you have one, or cook with unsalted butter.

For salads   Make your own dressing without oil.

Right, my Taurean friends, here are a few recipes for your first week. You can change them around as you like.

DON'T FORGET, TWO GLASSES OF WATER BEFORE EVERY MEAL

DAY 1   Fruit only plus your two glasses of water before each meal, if you can survive this day, you're on your way.

DAY 2   *Breakfast*
Bran with skimmed milk
Orange juice
Lunch
Steak and salad
Mid-afternoon
Your treat
Dinner
Shrimp, brown rice and stir fried vegetables
Slices of papaya

DAY 3   *Breakfast*
Two eggs scrambled
Prune juice
Lunch
One baked potato with cottage cheese

30

Dinner
Spaghetti with a sauce made of tomatoes, mushrooms and onions
Jelly
Your treat

DAY 4 *Breakfast*
Fresh fruits
Mid-morning
Your treat
Lunch
Two egg omelette
Dinner
Liver braised in tomatoes
Broccoli
Courgettes
Strawberries

DAY 5 *Breakfast*
Grapefruit
Your treat
Lunch
Tuna (oil drained)
A small salad of your choice
Dinner
Fillet of sole (poached or grilled) sprinkled with almonds
Asparagus
Slices of fresh pineapple

DAY 6 *Breakfast*
Bran with yoghurt
One banana
Lunch
Cold beef and horseradish
A small salad
Dinner
Chicken breast roasted
Mushrooms
Cabbage
One new potato (if you must)
Your treat

DAY 7   *Breakfast*
One boiled egg
Your treat
Lunch
Green pepper stuffed with mushrooms, brown rice and tomatoes
Dinner
Breast of turkey and almonds
Asparagus
One new potato
Fresh fruit salad

Good luck on your diet! Don't forget your glasses of water before each meal. Bottled still or sparkling water is best but if you can't afford it use tap water, preferably boiled if in a hard water area. Black coffee if you must.

GEMINI

MAY 22 – JUNE 21

Lively, loquacious Geminis lose interest in things quickly so I'll have to come up with some varied victuals for you. Let's start by looking at your good and bad points.

General Gemini characteristics

Gemini, the Twins, have two separate sides to them, dark and light. They're either bright and blabby or they're really morose and miserable. The positive side of the Twins is that they are lively, witty and attract people to them like bees around a honey pot whereas the negative side of Gemini is the exact opposite and can twist and turn the truth and be mightily mendacious. Generally, Geminis are intelligent, ingenious and great storers of knowledge. They chatter at speed and have sharp inquisitive eyes. Those eyes absorb all at once, never missing a trick! They are usually attractive types both physically and mentally.

At work, they can juggle several balls at the same time but can drive mere mortals mad with their incessant spouting. Ideally, communication is the name of the game and the best careers for Geminis are salesmen, telephone operators, writers and journalists or teachers. There are many jabbering Geminis in the telly world. (Chat show hosts would be perfect posts for them, except even their garrulous guest would have desperate difficulty getting a word in!) Geminis adore a good debate or discussion and will throw themselves wholeheartedly into it even if they weave a few whoppers in the process!

They make much better friends than lovers and these gregarious gems collect countless friends along the way but for Pete's sake preserve your secrets 'cos they'll spill the beans in a trice! I have a smashing Gemini friend who's forever on the phone titillating me with all the latest juicy titbits, and when we meet, she always wants to try something new . . . an exotic eaterie recommended by a mate, the latest play or that scandalous pub with the sexy male stripper! "Wouldn't that be fun," I hear her say!

Geminis constantly chase change, as their boredom threshold is low. These curious creatures are fascinated by fiddling with gadgets, videos and computers. Travel is right up their street and they feel fully at home in foreign parts as they learn languages easily and soon speak it like a native.

Gemini love life

Geminis are always falling in and out of love 'cos they're quickly bored with their amours of the moment, and to them variety is the spice of life. They just hate to be tied down. These charming captivating chameleons are capable of carrying on four or five relationships at the same time. (Phew!)

They are excitingly but exhaustingly experimental lovers, and many marry more than once. The Gemini man is a real lady killer and quite irresistible but irresponsible. There's something magnetic about his mercurial magic that draws you to him. Once he's charmed the pants off you and knows that he's won you, he'll soon start yawning and yearn to be off somewhere else. So, chapesses, if you want this terrible twin, keep him guessing and he'll soon come panting to your presence and flirt outrageously, even if he's gone off you. Even with a permanent partner, he'll continue to flirt away quite festively with all and sundry. He'll make a disastrous dad when they're tots but as soon as they're big enough to play with, this overgrown child will be like a big brother.

The Gemini maid is as bright as a button and even first thing in the morning, can chirp and chirrup faster than a sparrow, Groan, Groan! This mercurial miss can be an outrageous flirt but she has a serious soul. She's a chameleon, with lightning-fast changes of mood to adapt to each situation and this makes her a very popular popsie. Gemini dames may be ice maidens on the surface (with passion pulsating down below!) but possessive partners and passionate declarations leave them cold. She will have no time for dolts and dunces, and be more interested in your brain than your beauty. Gemini women can be fiercely feminist and believe in the equality of the sexes. They don't particularly shine as mothers preferring their children's minds to their physical needs.

Gemini home life

Most Gemini domiciles are disorderly and disarranged! This home will probably be bright, bustling, full of scattered books, all kinds of gadgets to play with and pandemonium everywhere. These sunny scintillaters consider cleaning house a time-waster and even on the odd occasion when they spring clean, it still looks the same when they've finished! Some Geminis break the mould and are very traditional, neat and tidy. They love birds, cats and dogs so there'll probably be a few browsing around like furry and feathery members of the family. My Gemini friend has two cats and a dog and they are treated like 'real' people.

Geminis like breadths of breathing space and dream about decamping to Devon or Dorset but they're better with city life as there is more to occupy their quick-silver brains. They don't entertain too often but on this rare occasion, will invite hordes of hungry people (get it over in one go) and offer a buffet with a blend of ambrosial booty from all over the world. Recipes reaped from their roamings will be in abundance. A sit-down dinner is anathema to these demented dervishes!

Geminis prefer munching with mates and variety is the spice of their lives. They will suggest going to a handful of different haunts in one evening and that's when the flab starts to form. They love a night out with a cabaret, a floorshow, that will hold their interest. They're bored by shopping, particularly in large crowded supermarkets, and discover good local butchers and greengrocers, so they won't have to twiddle their thumbs in a queue. If they shop in supermarkets, they go for instant foods and as they've not bothered to check the fridge at home, will probably end up with floods of foods they've already got! Geminis thrive on travel and when out and about they throw themselves into trying the local fare and plonk and say, "To hell with the diet!"

Gemini health and eating habits

Gemini's ruling planet is mischievous Mercury who motivates them towards multifarious projects, so they have no time to eat and ignore those hunger pangs. The exception is if you're born on the cusp of Cancer and then you'll enjoy cooking and eating more than your average gem of a Gemini. Generally Geminis have few weight worries. Instant food appeals to them 'cos its easy to prepare but some Gemini guys and gals are heavily into health foods and become veggies.

It is beyond the realms of realism for a Gemini to relax, 'cos inactivity makes them nervous and boredom makes them ill. These quick-silver characters have, no doubt, tried every conceivable way to lose weight from hypnotism to macrobiotic diets. Gemini rules the chest, arms and hands and they should be careful when touching machinery. Lungs can pose a problem and they can suffer from asthma and bronchitis. They also have a sensitive nervous system and 'cos they find it so difficult to relax, some of them suffer from insomnia. They must choose a happy medium, 'cos overwork can bring on exhaustion and inactivity can bring on mental depression.

Famous people born under Gemini

Judy Garland (very typical of this sign), Duke of Edinburgh, Ian Fleming, Bob Dylan, Bob Hope, Thomas Hardy, John F Kennedy, Marilyn Monroe, Cole Porter.

People born on the cusp

If you're born on the cusp of Taurus, that is the 20th to the 24th May, then you're luckier than your Taurean friends as you don't have such a love affair with food and attending weight problem as them. You're always on the move.

If you're born on the cusp of Cancer, that is the 20th to the 23rd June, unfortunately for you, you might have picked up the Cancerian craving for cooking and food and bias towards booze.

Your diet and essential foods

The secret in your diet has to be variety and if I put together a list of foods for you to stick up on your kitchen wall you might find it interesting to make up your own recipes.

Daily diet supplement

Your cell salt, Gemini, is Potassium Chloride which is found in certain foods. Deficiency can cause colds and bronchitis which you are prone to. I recommend you take Kali. Mur. pills which are the homeopathically prepared biochemically active equivalent and can be bought at all health food shops.

    1 Multivitamin with minerals
    1 Vitamin C (for those colds)
    1 Vitamin B Complex

Here is your list and I'll suggest a few recipes to give you an idea of what it's all about.

Fruit	*Vegetables*	*Meat/Fish*	*Other Things*
Oranges	Asparagus	Chicken	Yoghurt
Pears	Carrots	Veal	Skimmed Milk
Peaches	Sweet Corn	Sole	Cottage Cheese
Pineapples	Cauliflower	Halibut	Eggs
Plums	Celery	Tuna	Spaghetti
			(wholewheat)
Apricots	Green Beans	Shrimp	Parmesan Cheese
Grapes	Tomatoes	Salmon	Bran
Lemons	Spinach	Turkey	Brown Rice
Grapefruit	Watercress	Liver	Sorbet
Papaya	Broccoli	Beef (cold)	Horseradish
Melon	Lettuce		Jelly crystals
Strawberries	Cabbage		(sugar free)
Bananas	Avocado		
	Onions		

For Cooking   A tiny drop of vegetable oil. Use a wok if you have one, or cook with unsalted butter.

For salads   Make your own dressing preferably with no oil.

DON'T FORGET, TWO GLASSES OF WATER BEFORE EACH MEAL

DAY 1   Fruit only plus your glasses of water before each meal.

DAY 2   *Breakfast*
Bran with skimmed milk
Glass of orange juice
Lunch
Two egg omelette
A small salad
Dinner
Shrimp, brown rice and stir fried vegetables
Your treat *for dessert*

DAY 3   *Breakfast*
Grapefruit
Yoghurt
Lunch
One baked potato with cottage cheese
Your treat
Dinner
Turkey breast
Asparagus
Sweet corn
One new potato (enjoy it)
Strawberries

DAY 4   *Breakfast*
One boiled egg
Your treat
Prune juice
Lunch
A salad of fruit and vegetables
Dinner
Spaghetti (wholewheat)
A sauce made of tomatoes and onions
Fresh fruit salad

DAY 5   *Breakfast*
Bran with yoghurt poured over it
Grapefruit juice
Lunch
Cold beef and horseradish
A salad
Dinner
Fillet of sole (poached or grilled)
Cauliflower
One new potato (if you must)
Jelly plus **Your treat**

DAY 6   *Breakfast*
Fresh fruit salad
Mid-morning
Your treat

Lunch
Avocado stuffed with shrimp
Dinner
Liver braised in tomatoes and onions
Green beans
Melon sprinkled with cinnamon

DAY 7 *Breakfast*
Two eggs scrambled
Orange juice
Lunch
Your treat
Dinner
Roast chicken breast
Braised celery
One new potato (if you must)
Stewed plums

Well there's the germ of a diet, Gemini. Don't forget your water, bottled or still water is best but if you can't afford that then use tap water and boil it if you have the time. Coffee is out for you, but you can have herbal tea if you like.

CANCER

JUNE 22– JULY 23

Cancerians are captivated by eating and cooking, so dieting for them is dreadfully difficult! First of all let's look at their general good and bad points.

General Cancer characteristics

Cancer, the Crab, is the first Water sign and being ruled by the mysterious magical Mistress the Moon, so many Crabs are psychic and super-sensitive to atmosphere. They are easily hurt and will weep at the drop of a hat. When they're upset they become mightily moody, grouchily grumpy and scurry back into their ultra-protective shells. They can appear to be hard and defensive, but underneath it all they're sentimental softies. The Cancerians' lives revolve around their families and they care for them in a cosscting cocoon. They need a home and family of their own, to really feel secure and safe, and to know that they're loved totally and irrevocably. So, embrace your Cancerian concubine or courtesan, declare undying love and devotion, and keep reassuring them of your love with lots of cuddles and kisses.

Without this security and love the Cancerian will fail to function. With their passion for the past and posterity they collect memorabilia and like to dwell on previous happenings, and these habitual hoarders can drive their partners mad 'cos the cupboards are cluttered with their trinkets and precious treasures which they can't bear to part with. Caring crabs make close chums and you can always turn to them in time of need as their protective personalities make them perfect with people. In return, they expect your love and loyalty and if they get this, these clinging crabs will keep you close to their cockles.

At work, the Cancerian can be ultra ambitious, and they know where they're going, and are sure to climb to the top of their chosen tree. Working from their cosy nests is their idea of bliss. The perfect pursuit for them is catering for sumptuous banquets, 'cos they love to cook, or a cottage industry creating knitwear and country crafts. Crabs love home sweet home so much that they are loathe to leave even for a holiday. Their hilarious humour is hard to beat.

Cancerian love life

Once a Cancerian falls in love, nothing else exists. They envelop themselves and their amour in a world of their own, which is OK if your chosen one is a fellow crustacean, but disastrous if the desired one is of a more independent sign. Once they marry, they're hitched for life. They are fervently affectionate and excel at sex. If you're trying to catch a Crab, show him how family orientated you are and tell him how you fancy a family of your own. When they marry, these clannish Crabs may still run home to mum with their muddles, and this can cause furious friction, ill feeling and frightening flurries in their marriages. The Cancerian man is succulently soft and sentimental at centre and as the sign Cancer rules the stomach, the way to his feelings is very definitely through his food. His heart usually rules his head and he's a continuous cascade of emotions, he can even wax lyrical and write an amorous ode or two. He will be fantastically faithful to his mum and his lady love might resent her rival especially, if her Cancerian husband has been waited on hand and foot all his life!

Crabs like to put down roots and they rarely move their happy home as they are creatures of habit, and stay close to their familiar rocky shoreline. They are captivated by their kids and as even male crabs are very domesticated and love being in the kitchen, they will even cook their meals for them. Cancer, ruled by the magnificent maternal Moon, is synonymous with motherhood and makes for marvellous mums.

Although they are the best mothers of the Zodiac, they can smother-love their children and they believe in the more the merrier, if possible. Moony maids who can't have kids will probably adopt a child or keep a pet as a child substitute.

The intuitive lady Crab is sensationally sensitive and sometimes she gets swept away by her emotions and desires and can't cope with them. She can be toughly tenacious which is fine in her job but could be disastrous in a developing amour. The positive Cancerian women can be caring and compassionate, sympathetic and supportive to her partner but if she's negative she can poison everything with her overpowering passion and tenacity.

Cancerian home life

The Cancerian's home is his castle. It will be seeped in tradition and reflect bygone days. Souvenirs of happy holidays, or ornaments and objects from childhood will abound, and the Crab's passion for photography will be apparent on the piano or place of honour. The kitchen is their favourite haunt and that's where they spend their happiest hours. Cancerian folk love to cook and always keep a jam-packed pantry. They are proud of their gardens and love to grow fruit and veg so they can boast of their home grown victuals on their tables.

Cancerians like to open their homes to all their family and friends – when they say you're always welcome, they truly mean it. If you're invited to a Cancerian's house to share a beano, be prepared and don't nosh for at least a month before you go, 'cos you'll binge on a seven course banquet. Eating at home, to Cancerians, is an occasion every night. They love shopping and stroll thoughtfully through a supermarket, choosing produce with great pains. When eating out these canny Crustaceans like value for money. They love a tasty little bistro that serves decent sized portions but they also have a penchant for fast food places that dish out junk foods.

Cancerian health and eating habits

Cancer rules the stomach and many are prone to ulcers and indigestion. It also rules the breasts, childbirth and the reproductive system and many Crabettes have womb trouble and problems during pregnancy. Cancerians like to look good and are miserably melancholic if they're overweight. They blow up like balloons when rejected in love but deflate rapidly when their love is requited. They've probably experienced every dietary delight under the sun but none feels right for them. Some Cancerians do well in groups like Weight-Watchers.

Crabs find it difficult to relax 'cos they're so emotional. At some point they can have a drink problem, usually to drown their sorrows and this is disastrous for those delicate tummies. This watery sign also tends to retain liquid which leads to a bloated feeling and weight gain. Cancerians are also prone to bone disorders, arthritis, rheumatism and nervous tension through unnecessary worry.

Famous people born under Cancer

Julius Caesar, Richard Rodgers and Oscar Hammerstein, John Inman, Ringo Starr, Henry VIII, Rembrandt, Ernest Hemingway, Gina Lollobrigida, James Cagney, Tim Brooke-Taylor, Princess of Wales.

People born on the cusp

If you're born on the cusp of Gemini, that is the 20th to the 23rd June, you may have picked up the Gemini habit of snacking and nibbling your way through the day and with your Cancerian love for candy and liquor, it soon adds on the inches.

If you're born on the cusp of Leo, that is the 22nd to the 25th July, you may be lucky enough to have picked up Leo's love of looking good and watching their waistlines.

Your diet and essential food

Moderation is the key word for you, Cancerians, just try to cut down on your eating and drinking for a couple of weeks.

Daily diet supplement

Your cell salt, Cancer, is Calcium Fluoride and deficiency can cause brittle bones and hardening of the arteries and veins. I would recommend that you take Calc. Fluor. pills which are the homeopathically prepared biochemically active equivalent and can be bought at any health food shop.

1 Multivitamin with minerals
1 Vitamin C
1 Super B Complex with Zinc
Calc. Fluor. pills

Eat as much watercress as possible as it is full of calcium. Right, Cancerians, here is a long list of foods for you to choose from, just don't choose them all at once!

Fruit	*Vegetables*	*Meat/Fish*	*Other Things*
Apples	Onions	Salmon	Cheddar Cheese
Raisins	Asparagus	Tuna	Cottage Cheese
Strawberries	Carrots	Sole	Bran
Oranges	Radishes	Shrimp	Yoghurt
Lemons	Cucumber	Cod	Skimmed Milk
Bananas	Red Cabbage	Turkey	Brown Rice
Grapefruit	Watercress	Sardines	Spaghetti

Pineapple	Broccoli	Steak	(wholewheat)
Papaya	Potato (1)	Chicken	Almonds
Peaches	Sweetcorn	Veal	Jelly crystals
Melon	Tomatoes		(sugar free)
Prunes	Lettuce		Eggs
	Cauliflower		Low Cal Soup
	Mushrooms		

For cooking   A tiny drop of vegetable oil. Use a wok if you have one, or cook with a blob of unsalted butter.

For salads   Make your own dressing without oil please.

Here we go then, I'll put together a few recipes for you, just to start you off.

DON'T FORGET, TWO GLASSES OF WATER BEFORE EACH MEAL

DAY 1   Fruit only plus your glasses of water. You may feel hungry so don't forget your treat!

DAY 2   *Breakfast*
Bran with skimmed milk
Orange juice
Lunch
Tuna (oil drained)
A small salad of your own choice
Dinner
Spaghetti (wholewheat)
A sauce of tomatoes and mushrooms
Jelly
Your treat

DAY 3   *Breakfast*
One boiled egg
Your treat
Grapefruit juice
Lunch
A baked potato with cottage cheese
Dinner
Cod grilled or poached with almonds

One new potato
Cauliflower
Strawberries

DAY 4   *Breakfast*
Bran with yoghurt poured over it
One banana
Lunch
A small salad
Mid-afternoon
Your treat
Dinner
Chicken breast
Asparagus
Mushrooms
Fresh fruit salad

DAY 5   *Breakfast*
Grapefruit
Mid-morning
Your treat
Dinner
Shrimp, brown rice and stir fried vegetables
Slices of fresh pineapple or papaya

DAY 6   *Breakfast*
Two eggs scrambled
Your treat
Prune juice
Lunch
Low Cal soup
Dinner
Steak (well done) and lean
Sweetcorn
Red cabbage
1 new potato
Baked apple stuffed with raisins

DAY 7   *Breakfast*
Bran with yoghurt
One banana

Lunch
A salad plus **Your treat**
Dinner
Veal grilled
Mushrooms
Tomatoes
Brown rice
Fresh fruit salad

Don't forget your glasses of water. Bottled still or sparkling is best but if you can't afford that, use tap water and boil it if you have the time. Try not to drink coffee, herbal tea is better for you.

LEO

JULY 24 – AUGUST 23

Royal Leos' weight problem stems from too much leisure and luxurious living and their only solution is to leave off! Before I set you a delicious diet, let's look at your good points and your weaknesses.

General Leo Characteristics

The Lion is the undisputed King of the Jungle and Leo, the Lion, likes to be the leading light both at work and play. If this beautiful beast belongs to the local amdrams his flamboyant flair will flee from one of the students parts, 'cos he must be The Student Prince himself. Leos are the most creative of the celestial signs and if they're not basking in the spotlight in a local play because their many talents lie in other directions, then they throng to the theatre to admire other thespians.

Lots of film producers are Leos: Sam Goldwyn, Cecil B DeMille, Alfred Hitchcock, and Busby Berkeley. These superior lions love show biz and are often connected with the theatre in one way or another. If they're not the star of the show then they'll be directing. Artistic Leos are often designers, painters, film or TV producers, or something where they can use their creative skills. If a lively Leo has a dreary, mundane job, in their spare time you'll find them organising some stupendous shindig or soiree in aid of charity.

There are two kinds of Leos, the ones with beautiful blue orbs and thick golden tresses, their leonine mane being their crowning glory, and the dark haired ones with cats eyes. Leos are extravagantly exuberant and their boastful talk can quickly become swank and swagger, and full of hot air. Nevertheless, they are genuinely generous and love making folk happy, and that attracts people to their bountiful breasts. Leos love high living, and as a mate you'll have many a riotous and side-splitting night out with them.

Leo is the regal and royal sign of the Zodiac. The Queen Mum is a perfect example, that gorgeous gracious granny, always beautifully dressed with delightful hats, Princess Margaret is another imperial Leo and she is a great supporter of the theatre and the arts. Princess Anne is also a ladylike Leo and she certainly shows the leonine qualities of leadership. Leos love a bash and they adore showy clothes and unusual and sometimes flashy jewellery. Anything to attract attention to themselves! These flamboyant folk like to look fantastic and this can be enormously helpful when it comes to dieting.

They make good and generous friends and will go to great lengths to please you but never forget they must always be King (or Queen) of the Jungle. Leo is a fixed sign and they are lastingly loyal and tremendously trustworthy. A Lion in love will always put the inamorata before allies. The positive Leo can be warm and loving and bursting with fun whilst the negative Leo can be arrogant, conceited and pompous. The ruling planet of these fiery fellas and females is the Sun and they are certainly sun-worshippers! If they can't afford a winter sunshine holiday, they make sure that they top up their tan on their sunbeds.

Leo love life

Leo, the Lion, likes to rule the lair. When Leos fall in love, they want to share their happiness with the world! Mind you, these feline folk fall in love frequently and then it's romance all the way, flowers, champagne, the lot! They need to be endlessly in love otherwise they get down in the dumps, so if you have a Leo partner, lavish on them love and adoration, though that can strain the soul if you're the independent type. If a Leo is spurned or scorned they raid the refrigerator. Don't forget that the sign of Leo is an animal, the Lion, but although these passionate pussycats like sex, they're not like Scorpios who can't survive without it. Love is a much more splendid sentiment to the Leo.

Leo men are generally alluring leonines with a majestic mane of hair. Typical Leo men are Robert Redford, Mick Jagger and Peter O'Toole. They exude great strength of character and charisma. They can be stubborn but flattery will get you far! When they are smitten, they will shower the objects of their ardour with expensive gifts and treat them right royally. They will make loyal and steady spouses, and expect the same from their partners. These breadwinners of the family will take pride in providing plenty for their dependents. They will make fantastic fathers and they'll want a pride of cubs. Some Leo men can be hypocrites, and though he expects faultless fidelity from his lady love, he's not averse to having a fling or fandango himself – the flirtatious philanderer!

The Leo lioness is the leading lady of the Zodiac and they tend to dramatise everything into theatrical proportions. Leo ladies love to be flattered and flirted with and are incredibly impressed if you shower them with expensive gifts and escort them to elegant eateries. They love dressing up in gorgeous clothes and socialising and partying. When she's a mum, she will protect her young, like a lovely, loving lioness.

Leo home life

The lion's lair matters most in his life. It will probably be splendiferously showy and gorgeously garish with lots of bright Sun colours like oranges, golds and yellows laughing at you or, if a well-heeled Leo, instruct an interior designer to inject expensive style. Leos adore animals and naturally have a preference for purring pussies.

Leos love to entertain and they make hospitable hosts and hostesses. The most choice chamber in their house is the dining room. Their tables will display champion china, crystal and silverware and be piled high with peerlessly presented foods. I recently went to a buffet party at a Leo's house and the sensational centre piece on the table was a huge ice statue of a swan surrounded by shrimp and crab claws with the dips in ice-wings. Gorgeous! When they celebrate with a soiree there's no expense spared. 'Tho these lions are usually clever cooks, they chuck off caution and choose caterers for such occasions.

Leos love shopping for clothes and jewellery but when it comes to shopping for food, these bored beasts can't be bothered. They extravagantly 'phone their favourite delicatessen and induce them to deliver. Supermarket queues are not for these regal types, and they frequent shops who convey the purveyance! They will be familiar with the best caterers and eateries in town. Leos like their restaurants to be rich and refined, with a romantic atmosphere, good service and beautifully presented food. They specially seek out spicy food. Champagne and caviar are just the ticket and they always appear dressed appropriately for every occasion.

Leo health and eating habits

I know you, lordly Leos, you lay your paws on all the latest diet books and aids and have inordinate intentions but as you chew a choc that book languishes in the library. Leo rules the heart, and if they don't watch out, they can have trouble with their tickers. They really should moderate their mastications as they pile on the pounds so easily and that in turn puts a strain on those huge hearts. Lovable Leos have so many social events on their calendars that it can play havoc with their weight and probably work is likely to be a round of business lunches and cocktail parties to attend and those unwanted inches soon appear.

Leos are recondite relaxers and being a Fire sign it's important that they let off steam now and then. Other ailments that afflict them are hardening of the arteries, hypertension, varicose veins and chilblains. Lions are generally strong but they are prone to obesity because of their love of luxury, leisure and pleasure. They sometimes have problems with their back, spines and circulation through indulgence and indolence.

Famous people born under Leo

Robert Burns, Jacqueline Kennedy, Percy Bysshe Shelley, Count Basie, Walter Scott, Lucille Ball, Napoleon.

People born on the cusp

If you're born on the cusp of Cancer, that is the 22nd to the 25th July, lovely Leo wants to look good and although you may have picked up Cancer's sweet tooth when emotionally upset, Leo's vanity will vanquish in the end.

If you're born on the cusp of Virgo, that is the 22nd to the 26th August, vestal Virgos and elegant Leos both want to look good, so fortune favours this cusp for dieting.

Your diet and essential foods

Let's put together a dynamic diet for you, Leo, one that cuts out fatty foods, 'cos too much high cholesterol is no good for you.

Daily diet supplement

Your cell salt, Leo, is Magnesium Phosphate which is found in certain foods. Deficiency of this salt can cause headaches, muscle spasms and indigestion. I would recommend that you take Mag. Phos. pills which are the homeopathically prepared biochemical equivalent and can be bought at all health food shops.

1 Multivitamin with minerals
1 Vitamin C
1 Vitamin E
Mag. Phos. pills

Here is a really befitting list of foods for you to choose from. Stick it up on your kitchen wall and plan your menu for a week.

Fruit	Vegetables	Meat/Fish	Other Things
Raisins	Red Peppers	Lobster	Bran
Figs	Cucumber	Sardines	Almonds
Prunes	Tomatoes	Tuna	Cottage Cheese
Apples	Onions	Salmon	Walnuts
Bananas	Lettuce	Chicken	Low Cal Soup
Oranges	Watercress	Veal	Eggs
Melon	Broccoli	Turkey	Yoghurt
Pineapple	Asparagus	Shrimp	Paprika
Blackberries	Carrots	Trout	Brown Rice
Strawberries	Potatoes (1)	Sole	Spaghetti
Plums	Spinach	Liver	(wholewheat)
Lemons	Green Beans		Jelly crystals
			(sugar free)
			Skimmed Milk
			Cinnamon
			Sorbets

For Cooking	A tiny drop of vegetable oil. Use a wok if you have one, or cook with unsalted butter.
For salads	Make your own dressing preferably without oil

DON'T FORGET, TWO GLASSES OF WATER BEFORE EACH MEAL

DAY 1 Fruit only plus your glasses of water. You will probably feel hungry, so don't forget **Your treat**.

DAY 2 The same as DAY 1, got to attack your diet to make an impression.

DAY 3 *Breakfast*
Two eggs scrambled

Your treat
Orange juice
Lunch
Tuna (oil drained)
A small salad of your own choice
Dinner
Chicken Breast
Asparagus
One new potato (if you must)
Strawberries

DAY 4 *Breakfast*
Bran with yoghurt poured over it and a few raisins
Grapefruit juice
Lunch
One baked potato with cottage cheese
Your treat
Dinner
Shrimp, brown rice and stir fried vegetables
Jelly

DAY 5 *Breakfast*
Fresh fruit salad
Mid-morning
Your treat
Lunch
Two egg omelette
A small salad
Dinner
Melon sprinkled with cinnamon
Liver braised with tomatoes and onions
Broccoli
One new potato (if you must)
Blackberries

DAY 6 *Breakfast*
Prunes
Bran with skimmed milk
Lunch
A salad of your own choice

Your treat
Dinner
Trout with almonds
Green beans
One new potato
Stewed plums

DAY 7　*Breakfast*
One boiled egg
Your treat
One banana
Lunch
Small tin of red salmon (oil drained)
A small salad
Dinner
Lobster (because if you've stuck to your diet, you
deserve it)
Asparagus
One new potato
Slices of fresh pineapple

Well, there you go, you lordly lions, a few suggestions to start you off! Your creativity will conjure up more complicated combinations of chow! Don't forget to drink your water, bottled sparkling water or still water is best but if you can't afford that then use tap water and boil it if you have the time. Try not to drink coffee but if you have to, drink it black. Herbal tea is best for you. Try to banish the booze for a week!

VIRGO

AUGUST 24 – SEPTEMBER 23

Virgos, it should be plain sailing for you to diet, with your fondness for fruits and salads. First, let's scrutinise your good points and your weaknesses.

General Virgo Characteristics

Virgo is ruled by that mental magician Mercury, the planet of mind and communication and because of their untiring thirst for knowledge, they can go far along life's path. They're inquisitive and analytical and are ever seeking for proof of everything. At work, though hardly the most ambitious sign, they are careful, conscientious and industrious and usually successful. These dependable, diligent and dedicated types do well at jobs with responsibility attached, e.g. secretaries, doctors or nurses. A boss would be blessed to have a virtuous Virgo working for him 'cos they're totally trustworthy, self-disciplined and systematic, and will see a job right through to the end. They relish routine, these 9–5ers and and would freak in a freelance job as they need to rely on regular remuneration.

These modest maids and men are sheepishly shy in love. Virgos value perfection and they don't put up with pratts! A Virgo will penetrate any pretence immediately. If a Virgo befriends you, it's 'cos he's mad on your mind, as they love a good old discussion with swotty sharp-wits like themselves! They are convivial conversationalists and congenial hosts. They make selfless friends and in times of need, will offer oodles of aid. But when they're in trouble, they withdraw into themselves and prefer to be on their own.

Virgo love life

Virgos heads rule their hearts and they can be chillingly cold, dispassionate and undemonstrative. When they fall for a fella or female they find it difficult to show their feelings, and their amorous amours will be anguished and upset by their indifferent attitudes. They are terrified to reveal their emotions. These insecure introverts can't believe that anybody could be in love with them, so if your beloved is a Virgo, reassure them in a modest way and convey how much you care!

The virile Virgo man is generally, as the gypsy forecasts, tall, dark and handsome and their sense of humour shines through their twinkling eyes. This chap can be cool and shatteringly blunt. Their demeanour is distant and detached, but if you manage to manoeuvre underneath that icy exterior, you'll find loads of loving waiting to be set free. It would take a wonderful woman to woo him. Virgo males are quite happy living alone and even when they get spliced they need an abundance of space. They must marry a mate who's involved in their interests and who senses a sexy soul behind that natural reserve. This sensuous sign needs sex to relieve the tension. They weren't designed as delightful dads 'cos they find it so difficult to show affection and in schoolmasterly style are sometimes too strict with their spawn. Virgo Venuses are generally suspicious of sex and are frightened to fizzle in bed, so they need an understanding amour who will love and caress them and, vitally important, make them feel secure. Only then will the Virgo lass blossom forth and radiate that private passion. Virgo women sport simple and casual clothes, but even in a sloppy track suit, they look neat and tidy. They always appear fresh as a daisy and want very little war-paint! They make marvellous mums and revel in teaching their children to read and write, continually committed to improving their minds. Maybe a cuddle would count for more!

Virgo home life

Virgos villas are pristine clean, not a speck of dust to be seen. The decor, down-to-earth and country colours much in evidence, the harvest and autumn; corn and barley and beige. The living quarters well lit, and every stick of furniture will be functional – sometimes too clinical. No flibberty frilly things in this house. It will look expensively simple. The most important room in these fastidious folks' house, without doubt, is the bathroom, where they believe that cleanliness is next to godliness. They have a 'thing' about floors and are forever down on their hands and knees frantically dusting and freeing the garret from germs. The welcome mat is always waiting at a Virgo's home, and whether you warn them or walk in willy-nilly that spotless residence will be spick and span.

If you're due to dine, plan to be punctual 'cos these punctilious perfectionists get piqued if you're late! A meal at their maison will feature lots of healthy foods, like salads and home-baked wholemeal bread and the spread will probably be simple but superior. Virgos are easy entertainers but they find it tough to relax, even with close chums.

Virgos are efficiently organised when it comes to the weekly blitz on food buying. Armed with their exhaustive list, they know exactly what they want and where, down to the last loaf, everything is in the supermarket. These demons for details compare prices and save sous wherever possible. They read all the labels and refrain from foods with additives or preservatives. They splash out on household staples such as disinfectant and loo cleansers and of course, being health-conscious hypochondriacs, they purchase panaceas, palliatives and pills at the pharmacy. The only time they let their locks down and have a laugh is when they're dining out having posh nosh, especially of the healthy kind.

Virgo health and eating habits

Virgos can be hopeless hypochondriacs and overly obsessed with their health, taking potions and powders for everything. Their bathroom medicine cabinets carry countless cures and are usually choc-a-bloc. Overweight appals them more than any other sign in the Zodiac. Virtuous Virgos want their physiques to be perfect, and are careful about what they chomp and chew. Many eschew meat and become vegetarians and wholefood fanatics. Even when eating out, they are fiendishly fussy about their choice of chow, fully au fait with the pros and cons of every edible. They wind up putting on weight when overworking or worried 'cos then they become down and depressed and truly twitch with tension and that's when they forage in the fridge. Virgos' idea of heaven is a holiday at a health farm and they need regular respite just to relax and unravel. Virgo is boss of the bowels and all things abdominal, so they are prone to stomach problems like colitis, ulcers and ineffective intestines. These maidens are martyrs to nervous tension which can cause some of them to suffer from asthma. Generally speaking Virgos are very healthy.

Famous people born under Virgo

Leonard Bernstein, Greta Garbo, D. H. Lawrence, Sophia Loren, Peter Sellers, Queen Elizabeth I.

People born on the cusp

If you're born on the cusp of Leo, that is the 22nd to the 26th August, then you have considerably more control over your corpuscles than your partying friend Leo. Now and then you might deviate from your diet but Virgos' pursuit of perfection will bring you back in line.

If you're born on the cusp of Libra, that is the 21st to the 25th September, you are lucky lads and lasses to have homely hankerings in the way of food. Naughty Libra may have hampered you with a sweet tooth but your virtuous Virgo veerings will always reinstate you on the straight and narrow.

Your diet and essential foods

Let's develop a delectable diet for you, Virgos, one full of salads, fruit and healthy foods. This should be a piece of cake for you. (Forget the cake!).

Daily diet supplement

Your cell salt, Virgo, is Potassium Sulphate which can be found in certain foods. Deficiency can cause spots and acne 'cos the pores become clogged. I recommend that you take Kali. Sulph. pills which are the homeopathically prepared biochemically active equivalent and can be bought at all health food shops.

1 Multivitamin with minerals
1 Vitamin C
1 Vitamin B Complex
Kali. Sulph. pills

Right, Virgos, here is a list of foods for you to stick up on your wall. I have included lots of fruits and vegetables and as you enjoy them, you should have fun with this diet.

Fruit	Vegetables	Meat/Fish	Other Things
Apples	Cucumber	Veal	Bran
Bananas	Tomatoes	Tuna	Honey
Grapes	Lettuce	Chicken	Yoghurt
Lemons	Radish	Salmon	Almonds
Oranges	Onions	Steak	Cheese

Melon	Beetroot	Shrimp	Eggs
Grapefruit	Turnips	Sole	Jelly crystals
Raisins	Watercress	Trout	(sugar free)
Strawberries	Potatoes		Skimmed milk
Pineapple	Asparagus		Spaghetti
Avocado	Parsley		(wholewheat)
	Celery		Brown Rice
	Spinach		
	Cabbage		
	Broccoli		
	Cauliflower		
	Green pepper		
	Green beans		
	Mushrooms		

For cooking A tiny drop of vegetable oil. Use a wok if you have one, or cook with unsalted butter.

For salads Make your own dressing with no oil.

DON'T FORGET, TWO GLASSES OF WATER BEFORE EACH MEAL

DAY 1 Fruit only plus your glasses of water. You may feel hungry so don't forget **Your treat.**

DAY 2 *Breakfast*
Bran with yoghurt poured over it
One banana
Lunch
A nice salad of your own choice of the above
Your treat
Dinner
Melon sprinkled with cinnamon
Chicken breast
Asparagus
One new potato (if you must)
Strawberries

DAY 3 *Breakfast*
One boiled egg plus **Your treat**

Orange juice
Lunch
Tuna (oil drained)
A salad from your vegetables
Dinner
Shrimp with brown rice
Stir fried vegetables
Fresh fruit salad

DAY 4 *Breakfast*
Fresh fruit salad
Mid-morning
Your treat
Lunch
One baked potato with cottage cheese
Dinner
Sole poached or grilled and sprinkled with almonds
One new potato
Green beans
Fresh pineapple

DAY 5 *Breakfast*
Grapefruit
Bran with skimmed milk
Lunch
Beetroot soup (boil 1lb beets with an onion and blend. Dilute with
water if necessary)
Your treat
Dinner
Steak (well done)
Braised celery
Cauliflower
Jelly

DAY 6 *Breakfast*
Two eggs scrambled
Prune juice
Lunch
Green pepper stuffed with tomatoes and mushrooms

Dinner
Avocado stuffed with shrimp
Veal fillet, grilled, sprinkled with lemon
Broccoli spears with a little cheese
One new potato (if you must)
Dessert – **Your treat**

DAY 7 *Breakfast*
Bran and raisins, yoghurt poured over it
Lunch
A salad of your own choice
Dinner
Spaghetti (wholewheat)
A sauce made of tomatoes, mushrooms and onions
Fresh fruit salad

There, that's not so bad is it? Make up your menus from this melange and have fun with your diet! Don't forget to drink your water, bottled still or sparkling is the best but if you can't afford that then use tap water and if you have the time, boil it first. Try not to drink coffee, but if you must, then make it black. Herbal tea is rather nice.

LIBRA

SEPTEMBER 24 – OCTOBER 23

Librans' sweet tooth could be their downfall, but if they contrive to control that then dieting should be a doddle! First, let's scrutinise their saintly side and then try to sort out their weaknesses.

General Libran Characteristics

Libra is the sign of the scales and most of the time they're beautifully balanced and you have a lovely Libra! They are intellectual, ambitious and in times of crisis they are capable of cool choices. They usually understand what they want out of life and they have the nous and knack of nailing it. Librans' ruling planet is voluptuous Venus and that makes them charming, courteous, cordial and oh that cute dimpled smile can melt an iceberg.

They can worship work but if that delicately balanced scale slips out of symmetry then you sometimes see the less than sunny side and that's the lazy, argumentative, indecisive Libra. They are partial to a good parley and they've always got beak in book, so they're generally extremely erudite and eloquent.

These well-balanced folk are always open to other points of view. Many Librans go into law or politics and they make discreet and discerning diplomats. Maggie Thatcher is a marvellous specimen!

Librans make smashing sidekicks. They're fabulous fun to be with and they're so honest and helpful, you can't help but love 'em. In fact, they price their pals and partners higher than themselves. These selfless souls get very sore if they think that somebody dislikes them, and they demur at denying their dearest anything 'cos they hate upsetting folk.

My Libran friend, a marvellous mate, has two great faults: she can't make up her mind what frock to choose and will get the whole weighty wardrobe out before a decision is made, and she's perpetually unpunctual for our appointments. But I always forgive her, 'cos she bedazzles me with her beautiful beatific beam, says "Sorry." and twists me round her wee pinky! She is a typical Libran and loves everything to be opulent, plush and high class, costly clothes, the real McCoy when it comes to jewellery and of course, ritzy restaurants. Quality counts! (Just like Leos!).

Libran love life

Libra is the sign of marriage and partnership and Librans love to be in love. This is the variety of romance you dream about and only peruse in print. Librans will pursue their passing passions with bouquets and bubbly (they adore champers) and sweep them off their soles. Once they're in love, the world stops turning and like Mills & Boon, they hanker after happy endings and pray that their partnerships will blissfully blossom 'till death do us part'! But life ain't like that! Librans in love get all higgledy-piggledy and sometimes can't see the wood for the trees and if forsaken by their sweethearts, they become moody and morose, and the perfectly poised scales unbalance. If their loved one elopes with a rival, they tend to retreat and give up the fight easily. Peace at any price is their motto! They abhor arguments and will bend over backwards to avoid one.

The Libran man will charm the pants off you! They are courtly, chivalrous and cater for your every whim. They adore to dress well and like their women to be bonny and beautiful. Loving Librans generally welcome warm cuddles and closeness more than good old lusty sex. If you wed a Libran lad, you'll just have to face the fact that he's a flirt. Every lovely lady he meets will be a temptation to him and he sometimes succumbs to seduction and strays off the straight and narrow. Never, ever forget that beneath that outward charm, lies a cold, hard streak – the iron first in the velvet glove. They can be dynamic dads, not when the babes are at the coochy-coo stage but the second they're able to talk and communicate.

Libran women can be glitteringly gorgeous, and traditionally they're the most glamorous girls in the galaxy. The few that aren't endowed with these fantastic film-star features are still lovely ladies to know. They are flagrantly feminine and are those lucky souls who can look smart in sack cloth. This luscious lot love clothes and many of them favour fashion designing as a future. The only time you'll see a Libran lady looking a wreck is if she's unlucky in love. They need to be adored and they crave company and lots of companions. Librans don't make particularly maternal mothers as they're always rushing around and don't have the time to spend with their kids, but they will try to galvanise their grey matter with lots of books. If you want to win a Libran lady, send her a bottle of stunning scent. In fact, if you lust after a Libran, lad or lady, you have to look good, smell good and treat 'em good. The sign of savoir faire!

Libran home life

Sometimes, you go into a house and your mouth drops open in amazement. It is so indescribably incredible and exquisite that words fail you! Delicate soft pastel-shades of blues, lilacs, pinks and pale greens, all beautifully blended and combined with wallpapers and curtains. Fresh flowers that have been artistically arranged with loving care in pretty porcelain pots, prudently placed in alcoves or windows. This is likely to be a Libran lair. The number one room in the Libran abode is the boudoir and it will be tastefully and elegantly furnished with sumptuous satins, silks and scatter cushions all over the bed (probably a four-poster).

Librans are not potty on pets, the odd one or two might keep a canine but generally they steer a wide berth 'cos they make a mess! (And pong!). These well-balanced bods often live close to, or even in, a city 'cos with Venus as their ruling planet, they are inexorably drawn to the theatre, ballet, opera, art exhibitions and 'owt creative'. Genial Librans love to be in a group and loathe to be lonesome, and they often entertain at home, making charming hosts and hostesses.

If you're summoned to a sit down dinner at their house it will be the best of everything! and usually Librans throw parties for lots of people. They favour lavish buffets, the table groaning with goodies, hordes of hors d'oeuvres and wonderful sweetie-type dishes because sweet-toothed Librans can't resist delicious creamy desserts. If they can't do with preparing all these tasty titbits, they will turn to caterers. These gregarious guys and gals find any excuse to throw a bash and that, in turn, is an excuse to abandon their dreary diet! Librans love shopping for chow and spend hours in the supermarket, especially in the delicatessen, looking for unfamiliar and fascinating foods to try out.

They'll go anywhere to nosh, as long as it's in convivial company. I have a male Libran mate who is so madly generous that when we go out I have to get a round in when he pops out for a wee 'cos he insists on blowing his boodle every time! Librans will do anything for some bubbly but after a few ambrosial sips of the sparkling stuff, their diet tends to wing out of the window and anything goes! In a restaurant. they delight in being dressed to the nines and they also relish beautifully presented food. One Libran pal has a penchant for Japanese junkets, not because he particularly likes it but because it looks so lovely!

Libran health and eating habits

Unfortunately, Librans like the good life too much and find it desperately difficult to adhere to any diet. Librans are either pleasantly portly and plump or perfectly formed and well-rounded. It might be easier for them to diet in droves – Weight Watchers might do the trick. Candies spell dietary collapse and excessive drinking can be disastrous to your kidneys and bladder, your weak points. Librans need eight hours shut-eye a night, essential especially when you're overworking (which is all too often). Otherwise you'll be overtaken by nervous tension, stress and all stress-related diseases like headaches and ulcers. Librans are vulnerable to colds, flu, high blood pressure and back problems. They are also prone to diabetes.

Famous people born under Libra

Roger Moore, Julie Andrews, Brigitte Bardot, Charles Boyer, T S Eliot (Cats), George Gershwin, Charlton Heston, Franz List, Oscar Wilde.

People born on the cusp

If you're born on the cusp of Virgo, that is the 21st to the 25th September, you'll be lucky 'cos though you're smitten by sweet things, Virgo's love of wholefoods will steer you onto the straight and narrow.

If you're born on the cusp of Scorpio, that is the 22nd to the 25th October, your Scorpio single-mindedness will not let you lose control of weight for long and will help you fight that flab.

Your diet and essential foods

Try to tempt a pal to partake in this purge with you and you could offer each other moral support. You must lay off those sweets!

Daily diet supplement

Your cell salt, Libra, is Sodium phosphate, which is present in some foods and is necessary for the functioning of the kidneys and the elimination of waste matters. Deficiency of this salt can cause the stiffening of the joints and end up in rheumatism. I recommend that you take Nat. Phos. pills which are the homeopathically prepared biochemically active equivalent and can be bought at any health food shop.

> 1 Multivitamin with minerals
> 1 Vitamin C
> 1 Vitamin E
> Nat. Phos. pills

OK here we go, here is a list of foods to stick up on your kitchen wall and you can choose your own menu as you go along.

Fruit	*Vegetables*	*Meat/Fish*	*Other Things*
Kiwis	Watercress	Veal	Almonds
Grapefruit	Potato	Salmon	Honey
Grapes	Broccoli	Lobster	Skimmed milk
Apples	Tomato	Chicken	Spaghetti
Bananas	Lettuce	Turkey	(wholewheat)
Apricots	Cucumber	Tuna	Brown rice
Watermelon	Spinach	Shrimp	Bran
Lemons	Mushrooms	Sole	Yoghurt
Strawberries	Asparagus	Steak (lean)	Eggs
Pineapple	Cauliflower		Sorbets
Blackberries	Onions		Jelly crystals
Raisins	Carrots		(sugar free)
Prunes	Green beans		Cottage cheese
Mango			Low Cal Soup
Papaya			
Melon			

For cooking	A tiny drop of vegetable oil. Use a wok if you have one, or use unsalted butter.
For salads	Make your own dressing, no oil.

Here are a few suggestions for your first week.

POSITIVELY NO BOOZE FOR A WEEK AND NO JUNK FOODS
DON'T FORGET, TWO GLASSES OF WATER BEFORE
EACH MEAL

DAY 1   Fruit only plus your glasses of water and if you're hungry at the end of the day don't forget **Your treat.**

DAY 2   *Breakfast*
Bran sprinkled with raisins and covered with yoghurt
Lunch
Pineapple and cottage cheese
Mid-afternoon
Your treat
Dinner
Chicken breast
Asparagus
One new potato (if you must)
Strawberries

DAY 3   *Breakfast*
One boiled egg
Your treat
Lunch
A salad of your own choice
Dinner
Sole sprinkled with lemon and almonds
Green beans
One new potato
Jelly

DAY 4   *Breakfast*
Grapefruit
Mid-morning
Your treat
Lunch
Two egg spinach omelette
Tomato and onion salad
Dinner
Spaghetti (wholewheat)
A sauce made of tomatoes and mushrooms
Fresh fruit salad

DAY 5   *Breakfast*
Bran with skimmed milk
Orange juice
Lunch
Your treat

71

Dinner
Steak (well done)
Broccoli sprinkled with a little cheese
Mushrooms
One new potato

DAY 6   *Breakfast*
Two eggs scrambled
Prune juice
Lunch
One baked potato with cottage cheese
Dinner
Lobster, or if you can't get any, Halibut
Asparagus
A mixed salad
Sorbet
Supper
Your treat

DAY 7   *Breakfast*
Watermelon
Your treat
Lunch
Salmon (oil drained)
Tomato and mushroom salad
Dinner
Turkey (white meat)
Cauliflower and carrots
One new potato
Slices of fresh mango or pineapple

Good luck on your slimming session, Librans, and make up some smashing menus with lots of little tempting morsels. Don't forget your water before each meal, bottled still or sparkling water is best but if you can't afford that, use tap water and if you have the time boil it first. Try not to drink coffee but if you must, make it black. Try herbal teas.

SCORPIO

OCTOBER 24 – NOVEMBER 22

Steely and strong-minded Scorpios have enough will power to stick to any diet, so it should be easy for them to follow this one.

General Scorpio Characteristics

Aries and Scorpio are ruled by mighty Mars, yet they're poles apart in many ways. An Arian has a quick, fiery temper that flares up and fizzles out whilst inscrutable Scorpio will bubble just below boiling point and plot their revenge! They are dangerous and devious, and you will never delve into their minds. You try to fathom the depths of those deep, magnetic eyes but you soon get lost in the swirling pool and surrender.

Scorpios are secretive, assured and formidably powerful, so never underestimate them in business affairs or love affairs! These single-minded citizens see everything as either black or white, all or nothing, and they don't believe in in-between. Scorpios have a tremendous thirst for power and investigating ways to gain the upper hand. Many are psychic souls with X-ray vision. They go far in their favoured profession and as secretive Scorpios dislike the limelight, they mould and manipulate just as powerfully behind the scenes.

You will find them in the Police Force, or as psychiatrists and hypnotists, or any enigmatic job or secret service that is away from public scrutiny. There are also several stoical Scorpios (the Mars influence) to be found ready to fight in the Armed Forces. Be suspicious of a Scorpio soul-mate 'cos they will seek to exercise an emotional stranglehold over you. Accept that, and you will probably find a loyal and loving friend, who can be counted on in your hour of need, but if you ever betray them or go behind their backs, you will have made a frightening and fearsome adversary!

Scorpios excel at anything with an element of risk or danger – they are intrepid. I have a Scorpio lady friend who drives a racing car around Brands Hatch just for the hell of it!

Scorpio love life

Scorpios are sultry and sensuous and sex is as compulsive as eating, to them. They can wear out their amours with their energy and almost devour them with desire and passion! They often mistake lust for love and loads enter matrimony more than once after being thus duped. These passionate Plutonians are profoundly possessive and jealous and if spurned, can become vindictive and vengeful. The Scorpio squire has stupendous magnetism and with his black hair and penetrating eyes the weaker sex flock around him. Sensuous Scorpios are curious about the seamier, spicier side of sex but it doesn't really turn them on. They usually choose a female who's weak and willing and as partial to nooky as they are.

Scorpio sirs are faithful friends and usually make good dads but being a Water sign, they find it very difficult to demonstrate their devotion to their offspring. Scorpio women are often attracted to the wrong sort, but try telling them that – they have a knack of hurting themselves. Scorpio women are cool, calm and collected. They have seductive sexy eyes and, like the male of the sign, people are irresistibly enticed into their presence. Beneath that icy exterior, there is a whole percolating cauldron bubbling and boiling away, and they can be scintillating sex pots if Cupid is requiting!

If you cross or deceive a Scorpio dame she will never, ever forget and she will get even with you, no matter how long it takes. These chillingly intense and complex souls are nevertheless loyal and true to their chaps but they detest wimps and worms. Scorpio mums are mightily possessive about their kids and like lionesses will kill to protect their cubs.

Scorpio home life

The Scorpio residence is really warm with subdued lighting and super, soft rugs scattered about on the floor. They relish rich colours, like reds and burgundies and use them ravishingly when curtaining a window. The bedroom, of course, is their numero uno! Scorpios enjoy relaxing at home and love watching the telly or delving into a decent read, but every now and again they kick over the traces and go bingeing on a Saturday night.

They can get fixated about food and obsessional about booze and usually have a well stocked bar in their houses. Scorpios are smashing cooks and enthusiastically and excitingly create exotic dishes out of leftovers in their larders. They make intrepid travellers, and delight in discovering new dishes, favouring the spicier foods. When it comes to wine, they'll drink red, white or whatever! Scathing Scorpios are impatient with shopping, driving their shopping trolleys like racing cars and fuming if an incompetent or inefficient store doesn't stock their favourite fare!

Scorpio health and eating habits

Strong Scorpios are seldom sick but as they tend to burn the candle at both ends, they can end up exhausted, aching with insomnia and hankering to hit the bottle. Booze is the big bad beast for Scorpios 'cos it releases those simmering emotions and makes them air things that they deeply regret in the morning! And the demon drink makes the Scorpion put on weight. If their insatiable appetite for sex is unappeased, they will be driven to devour anything to hand, like a box of chocs, a bag of crisps or a packet of chips.

Bottling things up and worry is the worst thing for their weight. Scorpios' weak spots can be bowel disorders like constipation and haemorrhoids and they may suffer from serious genital organ diseases. The throat is another vulnerable point. Scorpios retain body fluids and need a mild diuretic. They've probably given all kinds of diets a whirl and had a go at health farm hideaways, and when they embark on each diet, they're unshakeable because they have tremendous will power. They love browsing around health shops.

Famous people born under Scorpio

Richard Burton, Prince Charles, Billy Graham, Grace Kelly, Katherine Hepburn, Picasso, Theodore Roosevelt, Marie Antionette.

People born on the cusp

If you're born on the cusp of Libra, that is the 22nd to the 25th October, this influence may have a calming affect on you and curb any pent-up anger.

If you're born on the cusp of Sagittarius, that is the 20th to the 24th November, you may find that fun loving Sagittarius may tempt you to transgress, but the Scorpio will strive for success!

Your diet and essential foods

I'm sure that whatever diet I'll design, you'll set your mind to it and see it through.

Daily diet supplement

Your cell salt, Scorpio, is Calcium Sulphate and a deficiency of this salt can cause stomach problems and also causes ovarian and testes problems. Calc. Sulph. pills are the homeopathically prepared biochemically active equivalent and I recommend that you take these along with your diet. They can be bought at any health food shop.

    1 Multivitamin with minerals
    1 Vitamin C
    1 B Complex
    Calc. Phos. pills

Here we go, here is a list of foods for you to stick up on your kitchen wall and then you can concoct marvellous recipes for your dieting week.

Fruit	*Vegetables*	*Meat/Fish*	*Other Things*
Black cherries	Onions	Beef	Skimmed milk
Prunes	Watercress	Chicken	Cottage cheese
Figs	Leeks	Liver	Bran
Apples	Cauliflower	Herrings	Yoghurt
Bananas	Asparagus	Sardines	Eggs
Melon	Radishes	Shrimp	Jelly crystals
Grapefruit	Garlic	Trout	(sugar free)
Lemons	Peas	Salmon	Almonds
Oranges	Green peppers	Tuna	Brown rice
Pineapple	Tomatoes	Lamb chops	Spaghetti
Strawberries	Broccoli	(lean)	(wholewheat)
	Sprouts	Turkey	Low Cal Soups
	Carrots		
	Celery		
	Parsley		

For cooking   A tiny drop of vegetable oil. Use a wok if you have one, or cook with unsalted butter.

For salads   Make your own dressing without oil, if possible.

Right, Scorpios, I'll suggest a few things for you for your first week.

DON'T FORGET, TWO GLASSES OF WATER BEFORE EVERY MEAL

DAY 1   Fruit only plus your two glasses of water before each meal, that should help flush away those excess body fluids.

DAY 2   *Breakfast*
Bran with skimmed milk
Orange juice
Lunch
Low Cal Soup
Your Treat
Dinner
Chicken breast
Asparagus with a little butter
Strawberries

DAY 3   *Breakfast*
One egg, scrambled
Prune juice
Lunch
Tuna (oil drained)
A salad of your own choice, from your list
Dinner
Spaghetti with a sauce made of tomatoes and onions and garlic
Dessert **Your treat**

DAY 4   *Breakfast*
Bran again with Yoghurt over it (got to watch that constipation)
One banana
Lunch
Your treat
Dinner
Trout (grilled or poached) sprinkled with almonds
Braised leeks
One new potato (if you must)
Jelly

DAY 5   *Breakfast*
Figs and yoghurt
Grapefruit juice

Lunch
A salad of your own choice
Mid-afternoon
Your treat
Dinner
Liver braised in tomatoes
Carrots
Sprouts
Black cherries poached in a tiny drop of brandy!

DAY 6   *Breakfast*
Grapefruit
Your treat
Lunch
Two egg omelette
A small salad
Dinner
Shrimp, brown rice and stir fried vegetables
Slices of pineapple

DAY 7   *Breakfast*
Bran and skimmed milk
One banana
Lunch
Carrot soup (take 1lb of carrots, boil with one onion
and beef stock cube, blend and add water if it needs to
be diluted)
Your treat
Dinner
Lamb chops (lean)
Cauliflower
One new potato (a special treat)
Fresh fruit salad

Good luck with your diet. Don't forget your glasses of water before each meal.
Bottled still or sparkling water is best but if you can't afford it then use tap
water and boil it first if you can. Leave off coffee but if you must, make it black.
Visit your favourite health shops and try one or two of their herbal teas.

SAGITTARIUS

NOVEMBER 23 – DECEMBER 21

Your trouble, Sagittarians, is that you perennially plan but then put off your diet 'till tomorrow'. Let's find a diet with lashings of goodies in it, to tempt you!

General Sagittarian characteristics

Free-ranging, fun-loving, Sagittarius. They are enthusiastic, optimistic, jovial, witty and candid. If sometimes they are too blunt, put their size tens in it and say hurtful things to friends, they don't realise they have wounded them. For example, "Whatever people say, *I* think you're alright." Then they're astounded when their amigo bursts into tears! But though clumsy and coltish both verbally and visibly, these maids and men are totally minus malice. Jupiter-ruled Saggies are very jolly jokers and can haggle the hind legs off a hyena or sell sand to a Saudi. Jolly Jupiter is the planet of luck and opportunity and charmed Sagittarians are constantly striving for excellence.

The sign of the Centaur is the hunter poised with bow and arrow but 'tho Saggies cherish a challenge in their lives, they're often way off target 'cos they set their sights too high. Sagittarians make marvellous mates and you can count on them to cheer you up if you're weighed down with worries and woes. But for goodness sake, take what they say with a profuse pinch of salt! They cherish travel of all kinds and they relish the ocean. Cerebral Saggies make good teachers, barristers or solicitors and many religious people have been born under this sign. They have a terror of being trapped or tied down by people or work and they shrink from a mundane office job. The Archers make good jockeys or gamblers as they love to hobnob with horses. These wise and wonderful wanderers are the philosophers of the Zodiac.

Sagittarian love life

Saggy males are the hunters of the heavens and these blokes are born bachelors, even after they're wed. They are heart-free and hate to be tied down. They are usually of the tall and fair variety with high cerebral foreheads, and being like Aries, a fire sign, if you want them keen, treat 'em mean! If you manage to catch a Sag give him loads of rope or he'll break free. These are not the doting dads of the Zodiac when their offspring are infants, but as their youngsters grow they find them fascinating and mentally stimulating.

Saggy lassies are often blonde, blue-eyed and flagrant flirts. These independent indivudals shun those shackles and chains. Freedom is vital to them and they should postpone being permanently partnered 'till they've sown their wild oats and hitchhiked round the galaxy. The perfect partner for a Saggy woman is a man who goes gallivanting all over the globe, as versatile and variable as herself. He must also be her mental match as this learned lady doesn't suffer fools gladly. Sagittarian women are besotted with their kids and bring them up to be as honest as themselves.

Sagittarian home life

The Archer's home will be cheerfully colourful and either pristine and clean or topsy turvey! They find housework a hassle but as they can't stand living in a slum they force themselves to flourish a feather duster from time to time. They like to be besieged by a bounty of books and as they love horses, they'll probably sport an equestrian picture or two. Some even dislike cats and I have a Sagittarian friend who sneezes every time she gets a sniff of our feline friends. With animals the bigger the better!

Sagittarians make super hosts and hostesses, and the Archerettes usually keep stacks and stacks of loose recipes, which they seldom get around to using, but if they're in a culinary mood, they'll whip up something exotic and spicy to fill you full up. Mostly these restless rascals find cooking as consummately boring as they find housework. They are short-fused shoppers and tear around a supermarket, tossing anything into their trolleys without bothering to compare costs. They adore eating out and favour first class food, fancy wines and convivial company.
Warning: If you invite a Sag to your home hide all the fine and fragile pieces! These are clumsy clowns! Calamity Janes!

Sagittarian health and eating habits

Sagittarians get over-weight if they overeat and it's usually around the hips and

83

thighs, especially on those sedentary Centaurs. Their love of the wide blue yonder leads them to try the spicier foods like Chinese, Indian and delectable pasta dishes – cosmopolitan cooking gets their cultural taste buds. These energetic archers work hard and play hard, ending up over-tired and becoming clumsy and accident prone. They may break the odd bone or two and that's disastrous for them 'cos they despise being disabled and dependant. Sags are also prone to chest ailments, bronchitis, diabetes and their nerves jangle when they've been overdoing it. Too much booze will cause liver complaints such as cirrhosis and hepatitis. Moderation is your key so don't bite off more than you can chew – know when to stop.

Famous people born under Sagittarius

Lots of Sagittarians go into show business, e.g. Jane Fonda, Frank Sinatra, Sammy Davis, Maria Callas, Walt Disney. Others include Winston Churchill, Mark Twain, Beethoven.

People born on the cusp

If you're born on the cusp of Scorpio, that is the 20th to the 24th November you may have picked up some of their steely self-control which will support you on your diet.

If you're born on the cusp of Capricorn, that is the 19th to the 24th December, the classical Capricorn would instill much more self control and discipline to help you along with your diet.

Your diet and essential foods

Let's put together a diet for you, Sagittarians. Positively no booze for a couple of weeks. Can't you hear your liver screaming "Help!"

Daily diet supplement

Your cell salt, Sagittarius, is Silica. Silica is necessary for healthy vision and a healthy nervous system and lack of this can cause nervous disorders, loss of memory and even cataracts. Silica also keeps hair and teeth healthy and stops brittle nails. Silica can be found in certain foods but it might be an idea for you to take Silica pills which are the homeopathically prepared biochemically active equivalent and can be bought at all health food shops.

1 Multivitamin
1 Super B Complex with zinc (Zinc is good for colds)
Silica pills

Use watercress as often as possible as it is full of calcium.

Right, Sagittarius, take the bull by the horns and say 'today's the day'. Don't put it off any longer, it's your health we're talking about now.

Here is a fairly comprehensive list of foods for you to choose from, so stick this list up on your wall and create a week's menu. You might learn to like this new, healthy you.

Fruit	*Vegetables*	*Meat/Fish*	*Other Things*
Bananas	Spinach	Beef (cold)	Spaghetti
Apples	Mushrooms	Chicken	(wholewheat)
Melon	Tomatoes	Shrimp	Brown Rice
Currants	Lettuce	Veal	Eggs
Lemons	Cucumber	Lamb chops	Honey
Oranges	Asparagus	(lean)	Almonds
Pineapple	Celery	Liver	Bran
Cherries	Cauliflower	Tuna	Skimmed milk
Strawberries	Cabbage	Salmon	Yoghurt
Grapefruit	Broccoli	Sole	Raisins
Fruit juices	Corn	Turkey	Jelly crystals
	Avocados		(sugar free)
	Sprouts		
	Carrots		

For cooking A tiny drop of vegetable oil. Use a wok if you have one, or cook with unsalted butter.

For salads Make your own dressing, preferably with no oil.

DON'T FORGET, TWO GLASSES OF WATER BEFORE EACH MEAL

DAY 1 Fruit only plus your glasses of water. You may feel hungry and if you do, then don't forget **Your treat.**

DAY 2 *Breakfast*
Bran with skimmed milk
One banana

Lunch
Tuna (small tin, oil drained)
A small salad from your list
Dinner
Roast chicken with broccoli spears
Strawberries
Your treat

DAY 3   *Breakfast*
One boiled egg
Your treat
Orange juice
Lunch
Carrot soup (boil 1lb carrots together with a beef
cube, blend it and water it down, if needed)
Dinner
Shrimp and stir fried vegetables and brown rice
Fresh fruit salad

DAY 4   *Breakfast*
Grapefruit
Mid-morning
Your treat
Lunch
Two egg mushroom omelette
Tomato juice
Dinner
Lean lamb chops
Braised celery
One new potato (if you must)
Strawberries again (your favourite)

DAY 5   *Breakfast*
Bran covered with yoghurt and raisins
Grapefruit juice
Lunch
Your treat
Dinner
Grilled sole sprinkled with almonds
Asparagus

Corn
Slices of pineapple

DAY 6 *Breakfast*
One egg scrambled
Orange juice
Lunch
Avocado stuffed with shrimp
Mid-afternoon
Your treat
Dinner
Liver braised with tomatoes
Broccoli
One new potato (if you must)
Melon sprinkled with cinnamon

DAY 7 *Breakfast*
Bran with a spoonful of honey
Prune juice
Lunch
A small salad
Mid-afternoon
Your treat *Whatever you fancy*
Dinner
Veal escallope fried in a tiny blob of unsalted butter
Spaghetti (wholewheat) and a sauce made of tomatoes and mush-
rooms
Strawberries

Well, Sags, if I can do it so can you. I would allow you the occasional glass of white wine or champagne but I know you, if you have one you can't stop, so it's best to go without. Don't forget to drink your water, bottled still or sparkling is best but if your budget won't run to it, then drink tap water and boil it first, if you've got the time. N.B. Try not to drink coffee, black if you must. Buy some herbal tea and try it, you might like it.

CAPRICORN

DECEMBER 22 – JANUARY 20

Capricorns, let's have a squint at your psyche, your good points, weaknesses, health and vulnerability and maybe create a diet that will stimulate and challenge you.

General Capricorn characteristics

Cautious, conservative Capricorns are disciplined, determined, dedicated and aim to achieve. Their career counts for everything in their lives, these workaholics of the world! They cherish a challenge but are cautious in business. Don't try to dominate, drive or daunt these hircine humans, and beware if you have one for a boss! Capricorn is the sign of the Goat and there are two kinds, the frisky and the stay at home. Some Capricorns appear to be grumbling, groaning, grumpy old goats but if people bother to scrape the surface, they will find they have a hilarious sense of humour and are a real hoot – giggly giddy goat!

This is the sign of status, responsibility and public recognition, and countless Capricorns reach the top after the age of 30. They make great politicians or local councillors. They like to be respected and revered, and toil to be appreciated. The Saturnine link with teeth and bones makes Caps good dentists (get your teeth capped by one) and osteopaths and many are mathematicians and scientists.

Capricorn love life

Capricorns are surprisingly bashful and backward in bed, but cascade them with cuddles and kisses and these earthy and erotic old goats become lusty, lecherous and licentious! Capricorns are horrified of being hurt in matters of the heart and are sensitive about their emotions. Once these horny creatures fall in love, they are lastingly loyal to their lovers and demand nothing less in return. Capricorn chapesses often choose weaker men 'cos they like to be boss and others marry men right at the crest of their careers as they like to look up to their men. No in betweens, for Capricorns. It's all or nothing. Capricorn women make marvellous mums and will adore their children and expect them to have the same strength of character as they have themselves. Doesn't always happen, ladies!

Capricorn home life

Open house is the order of the day for a Capricorn and it will probably be Victorian or Edwardian as they are heavily into tradition and history. Beautiful oil paintings and antiques may not abound, but you can count on it being comfy, cosy and full of wood – from solid oak to stripped pine. Capricious Caps aren't hot on housework as they'd rather be working. They generally go for the sombre colours of terra firma, like greys and browns with an occasional splash of sunshine or orange.

If you're asked to a Capricorn's abode for a beanfeast the table will be exquisitely laid, lace tablecloths, crystal glasses, silverware and beautiful bone china. Your tastebuds will tremble and your saliva stream at the aroma of the best roast you've ever had. I have a Capricorn companion who serves the most tasty roast pork and crackling I've ever tasted. (Help!)

The kitchen-loving Capricorn woman is a traditional cook and 'cos she hates to see food wasted she's brilliant with left-overs. This systematic Saturnine plans well ahead when shopping and knows exactly what she needs. She searches shrewdly for special offers and cannily saves money where she can. Capricorns love good chow but being homely hircines, they rarely end up at exotic eateries. They are rarely blind boozers 'cos they like to keep in control at all costs. They are not the party-goers of the Zodiac, but these get-ahead goats will go to any lengths to further their careers.

Capricorn health and eating habits

Capricorns are self-critical and pedantic perfectionists, not least in their bodies and they make darned good dieters, with model determination. These gambolling goats are usually hale and hearty but being world-weary worriers they bottle up their emotions. Because they are workaholics who cannot relax enough to relinquish responsibility, sooner or later their cool will blow and they will be martyrs to nerves and tummy troubles. They can also get bound up with constipation. These grumbling goats dramatise their symptoms and lots of them ham it up as hypochondriacs.

Saturn rules their bones and teeth and some Caps fall prey to painful arthritis and rheumatism. They happily hand their molars and gnashers (real or otherwise) into the tender care of the dentist, when other folk run a mile. Capricorn also rules the knees and that creaking and grinding sound is often an old goat coming down the stairs!

Some giddy Goats can't let go (try, Cap, you need to chew the cud like your carefree cousins), and when it all gets on top of them, they get tired and twitchy and forage in the fridge. The chocolates, cakes and candies they cherish are fatal when it comes to fighting the flab.

Many Saturnites have sensitive skins and are prone to skin disorders like eczema. Capricorn colleens are loathe to wear make-up for this very reason. Their spines are vulnerable, and its simple for them to slip a disc. They should take extra vitamins for their frequent colds. Capricorns are born with an old head on young shoulders but get more youthful as the years roll by. They will keep their distinguished looks and dry sense of humour.

Famous people born under Capricorn

Cary Grant, Michael Aspel, Frank Bough (Breakfast Time). Other famous personalities under this sign are: Howard Hughes, Joan of Arc, Humphrey Bogart, Richard Nixon, Helena Rubenstein, Ava Gardner. Faye Dunaway – typical of the Capricorn – high cheeks.

People born on the cusp

If you're born on the cusp of Sagittarius, that is December 19th to the 23rd, you will have more dogged determination than a Saggy and really put your mind to your diet.

If you're born on the cusp of Aquarius, that is January 19th to the 22nd, you will have the Capricorn determination to diet, and as the Aquarian tends to pick here and there you could create a diet that suits you to a tee.

Your diet and essential foods

Let's put all this information together and create a really good diet for you, Capricorns. One that's not too hard to follow.

Daily diet supplement

Your cell salt, Capricorn, is Calcium phosphate (Calc. Phos.) which is found in certain foods but it wouldn't harm you to take Calc. Phos. capsules which are the homeopathically prepared biochemically active equivalent and can be bought at any health shop. Calc. Phos. helps to build strong bones and teeth.

    1 Multivitamin with minerals
    1 B-Complex (for your nerves)
    1 Vitamin C (for your colds)
    1 Vitamin E (for your skin)
    Calc. Phos. capsules

Here we go, Capricorns, this is your diet. Remember the key word in your diet is *Moderation*.

Stick this list of foods up on your kitchen wall and work out a menu for a week.

Fruit	*Vegetables*	*Meat/Fish*	*Other Things*
Strawberries	Green beans	Beef (lean)	Almonds
Plums	Cabbage	Chicken	Skimmed milk
Apples	Celery	Turkey	Bran
Bananas	Asparagus	Fillet of sole	Muesli
Pineapple	Spinach	Tuna	Yoghurt
Grapefruit	Cucumber	Salmon	Eggs
Oranges	Lettuce	Shrimp	Cottage cheese
Blackberries	Tomatoes	Liver	Spaghetti
Mango	Parsley	Veal	(wholewheat)
Melon	Mushrooms		Low Cal Soup
Peaches	Watercress		Jelly crystals
Lemon	Potato		(sugar free)
	(not many)		
	Cauliflower		
	Broccoli		

For cooking	A tiny drop of vegetable oil. Use a wok if you have one, or cook with unsalted butter
For salads	Make your own dressing without oil. Let's take a look at your list and plan for a week.

DON'T FORGET, TWO GLASSES OF WATER BEFORE EVERY MEAL

DAY 1   Fruit only plus your glasses of water. This will kick you off to a good start.

DAY 2   *Breakfast*
Muesli with skimmed milk, topped with a few almonds
Lunch
Pineapple and cottage cheese
A small salad of your own choice
Dinner
Shrimp and a selection of vegetables (stir fried with a drop of vegetable oil)
Jelly (Birds make a sugar free jelly)
Your treat

DAY 3   *Breakfast*
One boiled egg
Your treat
Lunch
A salad (choose any vegetables and try to include watercress)
Dinner
Liver, braised in tomatoes
Green beans and cabbage
Strawberries

DAY 4   *Breakfast*
Grapefruit
Bran with yoghurt
Lunch
Wholewheat spaghetti
Sauce made of tomatoes and mushrooms
Dinner
Steak (grilled and well done)
One baked potato
Fresh fruit salad
Your treat

DAY 5   *Breakfast*
Fresh fruit salad

Lunch
Low Cal soup
One banana
Dinner
Melon sprinkled with ginger
Veal fillet cooked in lemon and unsalted butter and sprinkled with parsley
Cauliflower
Dessert: **Your treat**

DAY 6 *Breakfast*
Bran and yoghurt again (must watch that constipation)
Lunch
A salad of your own choice
Your treat
Dinner
Fillet of sole (baked or poached)
Broccoli (maybe sprinkled with 1 tsp. of parmesan cheese)
Peaches

DAY 7 *Breakfast*
One scrambled egg
One slice of wholemeal bread
Orange juice
Lunch
Tuna (oil drained off) and a salad
Dinner
Turkey breast
Stir fried selection of vegetables
Your treat

Well, Capricorns, there are lots of lovely foods to choose from and with your imagination, I'm sure you can create more interesting dishes than I have. Treat your diet as fun. Don't forget to drink your water, bottled still water is best, sparkling water is second best and if you can't afford bottled water then use tap water and if you have time boil it before you drink it. Create your own menu to suit your work schedule. N.B. Try not to drink coffee, black if you must. Herbal tea is much better for you.

AQUARIUS

JANUARY 21 – FEBRUARY 19

Airy Aquarius, it's your turn! Dieting shouldn't be too dreadfully difficult for you 'cos of your renowned iron will power. Anyway let's take a peek at your good and bad points first.

General Aquarian characteristics

Aquarius is the third and last of the Air signs and the two opposing types are very distinctively different. The Saturnine Aquarian can be a serious, respectable, revered member of society who will soar smoothly to the top, in his or her own conservative way, whilst the Uranian Aquarian is a controversial and contrary person always craving for constant change. This Water Carrier has some unexpected and outrageous aspects, occasionally going overboard for some outlandish cause. These are weak willies, and should never be put in charge.

Aquarians are most often fun folk to be with, and though these brilliant brainboxes may leave you bushed you will never be bored! These are the cerebral sharp-wits of the Zodiac and are, along with Geminis, the geniuses of the galaxy. They are eternally eager for enlightenment, and will drive lesser mortals scatty 'cos they always answer a question with a question. Many Water Carriers seek wacky, way-out work and their need for freedom is often found in self-employment. Air is the ruling sign of these inquisitive, informal Aquarians, imbuing them with inspiring, innovative and inventive qualities. But beware of an, obstinate bent!

Aquarian blokes are brutally frank and must always have the last word. They are exasperated by superficial cocktail chit-chat, and bland and boring beings bore the pants off them. Their idea of unwinding would be flexing their mental muscle in more intellectual games like chess or bridge. The Aquarian woman can be outrageously "one-off" and is definitely quirky and freaky when it comes to fashion trends. Even in wedded bliss this broad must have freedom and independence, and woe betide the man who ties the knot too tight! A typical Aquarian is actress, Vanessa Redgrave.

Aquarian love life

Aquarians appear to be detached, aloof and apart and this magic mixture attracts others to them like a magnet. Aquarians pick their paramours for their brains, not their bodies, so this magnificent male Aquarian Adonis could happily hitch himself to a homely, hatchet-faced but high-browed Hannah. As the thunder and lightning of the Zodiac, they can be excitingly electrifying and experimental as lovers, for as long as you absorb their attention, but these cool cucumbers can also stay celibate and single for months on end and stick sex on ice! Romantic relationships often restrain and restrict these restless rogues 'cos they flounder and flop without that Aquarian freedom.Aquarians are stable and steadfast friends and when they decide finally to settle for getting spliced, their vows will mean forever (as long as their loves leave them a loose rein!). Women Water Carriers also balk at this blessed bond and find it desperately difficult to adjust to a dual domicile. She is often the pillar of provincial society or the chief of a charity. She will treat her heirs as equals.

Aquarian home life

The Saturnine Aquarian is comfortable in a very traditional home (much like cousin Capricorn) and they surround themselves with solemn and sombre colours and a forest of wood. The Uranian Aquarian's home will be outstandingly original, ultra-modern and stuffed to the gills with all the latest gadgets. Every room will be strikingly painted a different colour. The Aquarian is the child of this modern age, full of computers, videos and electronic equipment.

If you get asked to an Aquarian's abode for a binge expect the unexpected – he'll probably provide a buffet or an exotic curry or chop suey. Your fellow guests will all be fascinating folk like writers, politicians, showbiz stars, 'cos Aquarians abhor being bored. Airy Aquarians hate routine shopping and will always try anything marked 'new'. Animals figure in Aquarian lives and most will manage a moggy or mongrel in their menage!

Aquarian health and eating habits

Aquarians rarely need to diet. You see this sign is so tied up in work and career that they don't have time to eat. Aquarian men tend to develop that middle-aged paunch after the age of forty. Because they are workaholics, they tend to overdo things and their nerves get gnarled as a consequence. The resultant stress may cause insomnia. If an Aquarian is stuck in a situation he can't escape from, expect him to stuff his face and experience a weight gain. Once they've put on those inches it's only that wily Water Carrier's willpower that will overcome the problem.

Aquarians are often health food freaks and they find a fad and follow it furiously. They appreciate salty foods, so hide your nuts and crisps when they're dieting or their determination will be all undone! They savour sour foods like pickles or gherkins unlike sweet toothed Taurus or Libra but folly lies in their fancy for souffles and meringues. Some Water Carriers have high blood pressure and poor circulation and others are afflicted with anaemia. Aquarian's ankles are their vulnerable points, especially when they are tired.

Famous people born under Aquarius

Paul Newman, Clark Gable, Alan Bates, James Dean, Charles Dickens, Somerset Maugham, Abraham Lincoln, Mia Farrow, Jack Lemmon.

People born on the cusp

If you're born on the cusp of Capricorn, that is January 19th to the 22nd, you may have picked up the Capricorn determination to lose weight and as you are usually too busy to eat, this could be a great combination.

If you're born on the cusp of Pisces, that is February 18th to the 22nd, then you might put weight on if you're unhappy in your relationships or romance.

Your diet and essential foods

So, let's put all this information together and suggest a suitable diet for you.

Daily diet supplement

Your cell salt, Aquarius, is Sodium Chloride (Nat. Mur.) Sodium Chloride is table salt and taken in this form it cannot really help you much. Health food shops sell Nat. Mur.

> 1 Multivitamin with minerals
> 1 Vitamin C
> Nat. Mur. pills (recommended dose).

Here we go and good luck. Remember the key word in your diet is *Moderation*. Stick this list of foods up on your kitchen wall and work out a menu for a week.

Fruit	*Vegetables*	*Meat/Fish*	*Other Things*
Apples	Asparagus	Shrimp	Jelly crystals
Figs	Aubergine	Salmon	(sugar free)
Prunes	Cabbage	(small tin)	Brown rice
Strawberries	Carrots	Sardines	Spaghetti
Juices	Celery	Chicken	(wholewheat)
Melon	Corn	breast	Lentils
Banana	1 Potato	Turkey	Wholemeal bread
Oranges	(per week)	breast	Herbal tea
Lemons	Broccoli	Sole	*No coffee*
Papaya	Spinach	Veal Escallope	Skimmed milk
	Watercress	Anchovies	Perrier or
	Radishes	Halibut	still water
	Mushrooms	Oysters	Bran
	Tomato	Trout	Eggs
	Leeks	Tuna	Yoghurt
	Green peppers		Cottage cheese
			Almonds

For cooking	A tiny drop of vegetable oil. Use a wok if you have one, or cook with unsalted butter.
For salads	Make your own dressing without oil.

ABSOLUTELY NO SALT FOR YOU, AQUARIANS

I'm now going to look at your list and create a week's menu for you.

DON'T FORGET, TWO GLASSES OF WATER BEFORE EVERY MEAL

DAY 1   Fruit only plus your glasses of water. This will be a good start to your diet.

DAY 2   *Breakfast*
Bran and skimmed milk
One banana
Lunch
Small tin of tuna (oil drained)
Salad (choose any from your list)
Dinner
Chicken breast (roast)
Asparagus with a tiny blob of butter
Your treat

DAY 3   *Breakfast*
Orange juice
One boiled egg
Your Treat
Lunch
Sweetcorn and if you must a little unsalted butter
Dinner
Shrimp and brown rice
Stir fry a selection of vegetables
Slices of papaya

DAY 4   *Breakfast*
Bran with yoghurt poured over it
Lunch
Two egg omelette plus
Your treat
Dinner
Wholewheat spaghetti
Sauce made of tomatoes and mushrooms
Jelly made out of sugar free crystals

DAY 5   *Breakfast*
Grapefruit juice
Prunes
Mid-morning
Your Treat

Lunch
One baked potato filled with cottage cheese
Dinner
Fillet of sole (baked or poached)
A salad of your choice
Strawberries

DAY 6 *Breakfast*
Bran and yoghurt
Orange juice
Lunch
Baked aubergines in a tomato sauce
Dinner
Melon sprinkled with ginger
Veal escallope
Your treat

DAY 7 *Breakfast*
Grapefruit juice
One boiled egg
Lunch
Sardines plus a salad
Dinner
Turkey breast (roast)
Braised leeks
Pureed carrots
Your treat
Fresh fruit salad

There you are, Aquarians, your first week of dieting. Quite an airy and appetising menu but use your own imagination, and it'll be more fun. If you're out at work, then your lunchtime menu must be created carefully. If you're enjoying this diet then start to include beef in your second week. Well done, of course! Don't forget to drink your water, bottled still water is best, sparkling water is second best and if you can't afford bottled water then use tap water and if you have time, boil it first. N.B. Positively no coffee or salt in your diet. Herbal tea is best.

PISCES

FEBRUARY 20 – MARCH 20

Pisces, the Fish, and lovers of all things to do with the sea or water. Maybe we can fabricate a fairly fishy diet for you!

General Piscean characteristics

There are two types of fishy Pisceans. Take those Jupiter-ruled Fishes, who are similar to Sagittarians with their zest for life and magnanimous make-up. They are extremely psychic souls with a sympathetic interest in spiritualism. Next come the Neptune-ruled Pisceans who inhabit a world of their own, way up on cloud nine. They are artistic, romantic and hypersensitive and many born under this sign are writers, poets, composers or dancers, e.g. those gifted gods Rudolf Nureyev, Mozart and Chopin.

Pisceans are creative and clever, gentle and charming but catch them while you can as they always seem to be floating high above you, and you'll scarcely get close! Jupiter ruled Pisceans are often connected with glamorous careers. They find creative outlets as TV or film directors or work for ballet or opera companies and like the adventurous archer, they love to travel the world. Those ruled by nebulous Neptune, on the other hand, have capacious capacities in the caring careers, like nursing, social work or helping the aged or handicapped. Shoals of scaly fish join the Senior Service, and are easily seduced by the sea.

Pisceans aren't wildly ambitious and will serenely settle for their own standards of success.

Partnering a Piscean can be perilous 'cos these Fishes are two-faced. Look at the symbol of Pisces, the fish swimming in different directions. They can be maliciously mendacious, machiavellian, and as the actors and actresses of the Zodiac, they exaggerate everything out of all proportion. Their concoctions are so convincing that they end up believing them themselves! You either get fed up with your Fishy friend because of his febrile imagination and foxy fabrications or you shrug your shoulders and accept him for what he is.

106

Nevertheless, these patient Pisceans are ultra-sensitive about what folk think of them and are very easily hurt.

Piscean love life

The words of the song, falling in love with love, is falling for make-believe, just about sums up these compelling carp! Women fall head over heels for the strong, silent Piscean man and because he seems to be other-worldly, he'll have a strange hypnotic effect on you. These Pisceans will treat you like a queen and will lavish luxurious gifts and gentlemanly love on you, but never forget that this two-faced charmer could be chatting up your closest chum! This secretive deceiver won't spill the beans, and you could be blissfully unaware of the betrayal! Piscean fishettes are attractive and aware of it. These duplicitous dames can also lead a dual life and marriage won't impede their amours. They are very caring mums but being non-confrontational these fishy females find it difficult to control their kids.

Pisceans have a penchant for pretty people and if their love's labour is lost these fishy folk are hurt and helpless. They might turn to tit-bits for comfort or hit the bottle and it could take years for them to recover their reason. Pisceans need strong, responsible and reliable partners to look after them.

Piscean home life

The perfect pad for our Piscean pals is a sweet little cottage, with roses around the door, close to a rushing river, babbling brook or the sounds of the sea. It will be cosy and comfortable as these considerate chaps and chapesses like folk to feel at home. The colour scheme will be the shades of the sea, blues, greens, and purples and their cushions and furnishings will show a myriad colours. The lure of the sea will be indulged with a fish tank indoors or a fishpond outside. These fishy folk love cats, so there will be a few furry felines around. Planning a meal isn't a piece of cake for Pisceans, but if they cook too much, they are very creative with left-overs. They only shop when the mood takes them as they consider it a bore.

The inner conflicts of the push-me-pull-you Piscean makes it difficult to pick a dish at a restaurant, and they usually choose what everybody else is eating. Pisceans are particularly partial to seafood and salads and if the eaterie overlooks the ocean, they're in seventh heaven. They love little Olde Worlde tea rooms and good old-fashioned home-made grub. Jupiter ruled Pisceans favour French or Italian nosh but Neptune-ruled Pisceans have the sea-dog's zeal for liquid libation! A well stocked bar will be part of the Piscean set-up.

Piscean health and eating habits

Pisceans retain fluid and the Fish often feels fat and puffy. If their nerves are jarred or they've been spurned in love, food and booze will dull the pain, and drinking can be a major problem. They are prone to liver complaints so avoid excess alcohol, which can lead to cirrhosis and hepatitis. Any slight to the egos of these sensitive souls can set them off on an ice-cream and chocolate binge, and when depressed, they will devour anything, even junk food.

Pisceans suffer psychosomatically and can be perennial pill-pushers. If they're under the weather they'll get pessimistic and depressed and maybe turn to drugs as well as drink. Pisceans try health spas, hypnotism and crash diets, but it don't come easy! The feet are their weak spots and they're prone to any foot problems such as gout, corns and bunions. Pisceans hate standing for any length of time. They sometimes suffer from constipation so increase your roughage. Their alcohol intake must be carefully controlled 'cos once they start, they'll drink anything.

Famous people born under Pisces

Handel, Elizabeth Browning, Rex Harrison, Michaelangelo, Renoir, Elizabeth Taylor, George Washington.

People born on the cusp

If you're born on the cusp of Aquarius, that is February 18th to the 22nd, you will eat if emotionally upset but you will eventually control it and go on a diet.

If you're born on the cusp of Aries, that is March 18th to the 22nd, although you're determined your diet must be one with quick results.

Your diet and essential foods

Let's put all this information together and come up with something special for you to include all those fishy dishes, you so adore.

Daily diet supplement

Your cell salt, Pisces, is Iron Phosphate which is found in certain foods and is necessary for healthy red blood cells. Deficiency can result in anaemia. It wouldn't harm you to take Ferr. Phos. pills which are the homeopathically prepared biochemically active equivalent and can be bought at any health food shop.

> 1 Multivitamin with minerals
> 1 B-Complex
> 1 Vitamin C
> Ferr. Phos. pills

So, there you are Pisceans, let's put it all together and form a diet. Don't forget the key word for your diet is moderation.

Fruit	*Vegetables*	*Meat/Fish*	*Other Things*
Strawberries	Butter beans	Lobster	Jelly crystals
Melon	Asparagus	Oysters	Brown rice
Pineapple	Avocado	Tuna	Sorbets
Papaya	Mushrooms	Salmon	Yoghurt
Apple	Broccoli	Herrings	Almonds
Prunes	Green pepper	Shrimp	Low Cal soup
Grapefruit	Celery	Chicken	Bran
Currants	Onions	Kidneys	Muesli
Bananas	Turnips	Lamb	Lentils
	Chick peas	Trout	Honey
	Tomatoes	Sole	Cottage cheese
			Eggs

For cooking	A tiny drop of vegetable oil. Use a wok if you have one, or cook with unsalted butter.
For salads	Make your own dressing without oil.

Stick this list up on your kitchen wall and plan your menu for a week.

DON'T FORGET, TWO GLASSES OF WATER BEFORE EVERY MEAL

DAY 1   Fruit only plus your glasses of water. Let's get rid of the excess fluids in your body.

DAY 2   *Breakfast*
Muesli with yoghurt
Lunch
Tuna (drain off oil)
A salad of your own choice
Dinner
Roast lamb
Butter beans
Your treat
Strawberries

DAY 3   *Breakfast*
One boiled egg
Your treat
Orange juice
Lunch
Low Cal soup
A salad
Dinner
Shrimp, brown rice, almonds
Stir fried with a selection of vegetables
Slices of papaya

DAY 4   *Breakfast*
Bran and honey
One banana sliced over the top
Lunch
Small tin of salmon
Tomato and onion salad
Dinner
Chicken breast
Asparagus with a little St Ivel Gold
Chick peas
Fresh fruit salad
Your treat

DAY 5   *Breakfast*
Prunes with yoghurt

Lunch
Your treat
Dinner
Fillet of sole (poached or baked)
Broccoli with a little parmesan cheese
A salad of your own choice
Lemon sorbet

DAY 6 *Breakfast*
Scrambled egg (one egg)
Grapefruit juice
Lunch
Green pepper stuffed with tomatoes and mushrooms
Your treat
Dinner
Lobster would be nice or oysters
Served with a salad and some asparagus
Melon sprinkled with ginger

DAY 7 *Breakfast*
Muesli with yoghurt
Orange juice
Lunch
Pineapple and cottage cheese and a little salad
Dinner
Trout cooked in a little butter and almonds
Butter beans
Your treat
Jelly made out of sugar free crystals

Well, Pisceans, that should satisfy your fishy tastes. If you're successful the first week, then introduce turkey and beef (well done) in the second week. Don't forget to drink your water, bottled still water is the best, bottled sparkling water is second best and if you can't afford bottled water then use tap water and if you have time, boil it first. N.B. Try not to drink coffee, herbal tea is better for you.

SUMMARY

Well, by now you'll have sussed out the secret of successful dieting – you must be psychologically attuned to wanting to lose weight – moderation and determination, in equally enormous shares! Makes sense, doesn't it? Force yourself to stand in front of a mirror, totally starkers, turn this way and that and he honestly open with yourself. If the answer is YUKK! then you're the only one who can do anything about it. The characteristics of the Sun signs are very general in this book, 'cos I'd have to do individual charts to get an accurate picture of every person.

If you're out at work during the daytime, it is difficult to stick to a diet and I've tried to make the lunches quite simple. I decided to market research a cross section of the public, to peruse their lunching practices and I was horrified to discover that more than half of you went without lunch 'cos you didn't have time. That's inviting trouble 'cos that tummy needs something to work on, however little. Try to toss back a bowl of soup or some salad or fresh fruit just to sustain you throughout the afternoon. Here is a list of people I spoke to:

	MALE	FEMALE
ARIES	Baked potato	Salad
TAURUS	Nothing	Nothing
GEMINI	Anything, usually in a pub	Sandwich of anything
CANCER	Cooked lunch or nothing	Sandwich of anything
LEO	Nothing	Nothing
VIRGO	Cheese sandwich	Sandwich of anything
LIBRA	Shepherds pie, or Sausage and mash, pint of beer	Sandwich or nothing
SCORPIO	Baked potato at a pub	Sandwich of anything
SAGITTARIUS	Something hot at a pub	Bowl of soup
CAPRICORN	Nothing	Bits and pieces
AQUARIUS	Hot pie at a pub	Toasted sandwich
PISCES	Tuna sandwich	Tuna sandwich

Fascinating, isn't it? Too much bread for my liking. Maybe it's time for you to start summoning up some self control. It's a fantastic feeling when suddenly you need a smaller size skirt or trousers. You become a different individual, much more contented and confident. Go the Grant way and give it a whirl.

CALORIE COUNTER

Apple (raw 4 oz)	39	Glucose (1 oz)	90
Asparagus (boiled, 2 oz)	6	Ham salad (2 oz slice)	155
Bacon (fried 1 oz)	170	Ice cream (vanilla, 4 oz)	225
Baked beans (2 oz)	51	Kipper (4 oz)	125
Beef (roast, in restaurant)	250	Lamb (roast, 2 oz)	150
Beef steak (rare 8 oz)	700	Lard (1 oz)	260
Beefburger (2 oz without bun)	35	Liqueurs (pub measure)	80
Beer (cheap, pint)	170	Liver (fried, 4 oz)	285
Beer (strong ½ pint)	210	Marmite (½ oz)	1
Boiled egg	67	Milk (½ litre)	325
Brazil nuts (2 oz in shells)	165	Mushrooms (raw 4 oz)	8
Cabbage (cooked, 3 oz)	7	Onions (boiled 2 oz)	8
Carrot (raw)	20	Orange (4 oz inc peel)	30
Carrot soup (per serving)	85	Oyster (raw without sauce inc	
Cauliflower (cooked, 3 oz)	9	shell)	5
Cheese (cheddar, 2 oz)	240	Parsley sauce (1 oz)	40
Cheese (cottage, 2 oz)	65	Pasta (uncooked per oz)	105
Cheese (Dutch, 2 oz)	185	Peaches (canned, 4 oz)	100
Chicken (roast 4 oz)	125	Peanuts (2 oz)	340
Chicory (2 oz)	6	Pear (raw 4 oz)	15
Chocolate (milk, 2 oz bar)	330	Pork chop (4 oz inc bone)	510
Cider (cheap, ½ pint)	110	Pork sausage	185
Cider (vintage, ½ pint)	275	Pulses (3 oz dried, boiled)	85
Coffee (real or synthetic, black)	0	Raspberries (2 oz)	15
Crisps (per small packet)	150	Rice (boiled 3 oz)	105
Currants (1 oz)	8	Salmon (2 oz tin)	80
Digestive biscuits (2 oz pack)	275	Scrambled egg (each)	90
Duck (roast 2 oz)	100	Soused herring (6 oz)	300
Fish pâté on toast (restaurant)	230	Spirits (pub measure)	60
Fruit salad (restaurant portion)	150	Sponge cake (3 oz slice)	260

Squash (per oz, undiluted)	37	Wheatgerm (1 oz)	105
Sugar (1 oz)	115	Whelks (with shells, 2 oz)	8
Sultanas (1 oz)	70	Wine (red, pub glass)	95
Tea (served Russian)	0	Wine (white, pub glass)	105
Toast and honey (1 slice)	100	Yoghurt (single tub with fruit)	150
Tomato soup (per serving)	90